WOMAN OF SUBSTANCES

WOMAN OF SUBSTANCES

A JOURNEY INTO ADDICTION AND TREATMENT

JENNY VALENTISH

Published by Black Inc.,
an imprint of Schwartz Publishing Pty Ltd
Level 1, 221 Drummond Street
Carlton VIC 3053, Australia
enquiries@blackincbooks.com
www.blackincbooks.com

National Library of Australia Cataloguing-in-Publication entry
Creator: Valentish, Jenny, 1975- author.
Woman of substances: a journey into addiction and treatment /
Jenny Valentish.
9781863959223 (paperback)
9781925435573 (ebook)
Women--Drug use--Australia. Women--Alcohol use--Australia.
Women drug addicts--Rehabilitation. Women alcoholics--Rehabilitation.
Self-destructive behavior. Rehabilitation centers--Australia.

Cover design by Peter Long
Text design and typesetting by Tristan Main

An earlier version of '52 Observations' was published
in *The Big Issue*, 31 Aug–13 Sept 2010
Some sections of chapter two first appeared in Tamara Sheward & Jenny Valentish
(eds), *Your Mother Would Be Proud: True Tales of Mayhem and Misadventure*
(Allen & Unwin, 2009).

Printed in Australia by McPherson's Printing Group.

It takes
dedication

CONTENTS

PART THREE: WOMAN'S LIB

INTRODUCTION

Women drink and take drugs because it's fun. They do it to be bulletproof. To be more intimate, or more intimidating. To become themselves-to-the-power-of-ten. To experiment. To enhance sexual performance, or work performance. To bolster relationships with peers and partners. To be social. To belong. To lose weight. To unwind. To self-soothe. To wake. To sleep. For most people, for the most part, substance use is a manageable aspect of life. This book focuses on more problematic use, whether that be through dependence or just the severity of the outcomes.

In late 2008, I pitched a book along the lines of *Woman of Substances* to an agent. She suggested we thrash out the finer details at a bookshop cafe in Bondi, so I flew to Sydney the day before our appointment, dropped my suitcase at an absent friend's apartment, and went out with another mate to celebrate my impending deal.

The next day I came to, naked, the front door open, a bad feeling. The agent had given up waiting in the cafe after an hour. Later, on the phone, we agreed the time might not be right. More pressingly, I had to find my friend's cats and book a new flight. Don't worry – we all made it home.

In late 2009 I pitched it to a different agent. Now I had quit drinking, but I didn't know who I was anymore. The agent wanted an assurance that there would be redemption, and there I was fantasising about buying a length of rope. She wanted a memoir (and, no, a 'novel' wouldn't cut it), while I wanted answers. Why am I governed by impulsivity? Why the constant restlessness? Why the urge to always press the big red button, even when it flies in the face of common sense?

I thought the answers ought to come from evidence-based research. So in 2015 I brought the idea of a research–memoir hybrid about women and substances (which includes drugs, alcohol and tobacco) to Black Inc. It was now approaching seven years since I'd quit drinking and redesigned my life, and I hoped to have the benefit of hindsight and distance. Even so, as the project progressed, it became way more personal and taxing than I had anticipated.

This was because the more experts I interviewed – doctors, researchers, clinicians, policy makers – the more I saw the commonality between my more distressing experiences and the path that plays out for many women whose substance use has become problematic. There were definite themes. It seemed negligent not to explore those parts of my history.

Yet the real revelations come from the drug and alcohol researchers and professionals. I travelled around Australia to piece together their individual expertise and form a bigger picture about the issues particularly pertinent to women, including:

self-soothing shame; self-medicating anxiety and depression; the link with eating disorders and self-harm; the propensity to be drawn to abusive situations; the stigma around dependent mothers; the physical issues that women in particular can develop; and the fact that the treatment industry is still geared towards the male experience.

Why do certain people become addicted?

There's no definitive answer. If there were, I would have turned it into a rhyme and trademarked it. One widely held assumption – if you poll the people either side of you – is that addiction is hereditary. Sure, it often is – in part – but only in that you'll have inherited poor impulse control, or some features that make you more vulnerable to stress, such as anxiety, sensitivity to rejection, and low frustration tolerance. There's no single gene for addiction.

To delve a little deeper, and with reference to epigenetics, within our DNA there are 'switches' that activate or deactivate certain genes. Sometimes this change of gene expression is triggered by physical development – say, puberty or menopause – sometimes by stress and exposure to a drug. Most relevantly to this book, repeated substance use can cause neuroadaptive changes in the brain that are the basis for craving, binging, tolerance and withdrawal.

Every year a new study seems to crack the code of addiction by isolating genetic anomalies in people with very severe dependence. The findings are then applied to larger populations of substance users, as though the explanation is that we must *all* have dopamine deficiency or a polymorphism of a certain gene.

The thing is, there's a huge spectrum of problems around substance use, and most individuals who wind up feeling desperate and wondering if they should quit aren't so dependent that only their genetic code could have programmed them that way (in fact, it's estimated that only twenty per cent of drug users meet the criteria for dependence). Consider the person who witnessed alcohol-fuelled domestic violence as a kid and then goes on to re-enact the same as an adult, but only on pay day. Or the person who takes a stranger home every Friday night, but could only be classified as a weekend binge-drinker. Or the person with anxiety who doses themselves with drugs to be a more natural conversationalist ... until it's impossible to imagine ever speaking sober. It's certainly possible to be a problem drinker or drug user without being 'addicted'.

There's also a theory that addiction is a disease. The American Medical Association favours this 'medical model', with the view that addiction causes changes in the brain that remain for a long time, even after substance use has ceased. It's also the view favoured by Alcoholics and Narcotics Anonymous, who believe the 'addict' is thus powerless over their use. In the US it's necessary to have substance dependence classified as a 'chronic relapsing brain disease' in order to have treatment covered by private health insurance. For the same reason, obesity is classified as a disease. Additionally a disease is, in theory, treatable by drugs, which keeps the big pharmaceutical companies happy. Some professionals also feel the disease model is kinder on clients and their families, as it diminishes stigma and responsibility.

In Australia, the disease theory isn't as popular. Here, policy and treatment largely align to the public health model, which posits that addiction is learned behaviour, and a complex interaction between the individual's biological, psychological and environmental factors, and the drug.

What's obvious to me is that addiction arises from a melting pot of factors spanning both nature and nurture. It can be influenced by availability; cultural messages; peer pressure; policy; social learning; adversity; mental illness; and temperament or personality traits. It's a biopsychosocial soup, and that's the script this book follows.

A note on language

The language of drug and alcohol use depends on what school of thought you align with. In the US, where treatment is predominantly based around abstinence, terms such as 'alcoholic', 'addiction', 'substance abuse', 'sober', 'clean', and 'recovery' are used, and have infiltrated the policy of many other countries.

In Australia, where drug strategy is based around harm-minimisation, the preferred language is: 'person affected by drug use', 'problematic substance use', 'drug-related harm', 'giving up', and 'level of dependence'. These are terms that don't create an us-versus-them divide.

I personally don't call myself an 'alcoholic' or – to coin an increasingly popular phrase in the US – 'identify as an addict', because surely accepting a label disregards every other part of our multifaceted selves and keeps us forever in a box. I'm also far too English to use a dramatic term such as 'in recovery'. However, in the subtitle of this book I use the term 'addiction' because it is less laboured than the alternatives.

Also it should be noted that when the word 'woman' is used, the context applies to all people identifying as women. When the word 'female' is used, the context applies only to those assigned female at birth, unless discussing pregnancy-related issues.

Some names have been changed throughout this book.

PART ONE

PREDICTORS OF A PROBLEM

1

THE PETRI DISH OF YOU

How childhood temperament can foreshadow substance use

It was 1982. The UK. The Falklands War erupted. The lowest temperature on record was captured by a lonely weather station in east Scotland, at -27.2°C. Unemployment exceeded three million, the highest since the 1930s. The IRA bombed Hyde Park and Regents Park, killing eight and wounding forty-seven. Thatcher's Tories were top of the opinion polls. In every kid's Christmas stocking there was a copy of *When the Wind Blows*, depicting a nuclear attack on the UK by the Soviet Union. I was seven.

I don't want to lose your sense of intrigue straight off the bat, but I was a sickly child, matted with eczema and, later, permanently trailing a hankie. The umbilical cord had noosed around my neck upon my grand entrance, rendering me mute. I brought with me a special delivery of postnatal depression and was soon registered as 'failure to thrive'.

Around our house they called me the Grizzler. My superpowers included a sixth sense for the acutely unfair, and internal combustions at perceived slights. My parents also bandied around 'sulking', or 'sulking again', but those words didn't do it justice. When wronged, their youngest child was a kamikaze pilot in a nosedive, unwilling or unable to pull up. Empires should collapse.

'It's not the end of the world!' Mum would exclaim, in an ascending tone. Dad's favoured description of Mum was 'wittering'. Mum's nickname for Dad was 'Eeyore'. We all did the Myer Briggs personality test one time and came out as introverts with tempers rising. Long car journeys were marked by the sucking of teeth, bursts of road rage and the odd hiss of 'tedious' or 'bollocks'; a Mexican wave of low frustration tolerance between the two front seats. It kept me on high alert, every tut triggering a spike of cortisol.

Sometimes I'd study Dad's eyes in the rear-view mirror as he steered us through European holidays of crumbling ruins. His handsome brows would draw upwards in an expression even a child could recognise as aggrieved. Some silent cinefilm of lost chances seemed to be looping eternally. Trying to smoke us out of the picture with repeated stabs at the cigarette lighter only served to jack a bit of dopamine out of those rusty neurons. He'd take the edge off by shoving Olivia Newton-John in the tape deck.

I liked to creep out my family in this way: sitting bolt upright in the back seat until they noticed me watching, nibbling on a plait. As a journalist I've made a career of it. Sometimes I'd lie down and cry undetected into the upholstery of the back seat, lost in some tragic fantasy involving one of their deaths. Outside of the car, we all kept to ourselves.

It's fair to note that we are English, but there was more to the sense of foreboding than that. My mother worked in the community services sector and my father was descended from a long line of Essex cops – a paradoxical dynamic right there – though he pursued the dark art of marketing. Our house itself was a police state, which Mum would attribute to his childhood when he was out of earshot. It meant our mealtime manoeuvres were closely scrutinised for plebian plate scraping, too few chews, or using our forks like shovels. Some Sunday lunchtimes a tear might plop into my wholemeal apple crumble; but discreetly, since governance operated under the popular wartime maxim: 'Children should be seen and not heard.'

My older brother and I got lots of advice like that. 'Patience is a virtue.' 'Do as I say, not as I do.' All variations of 'shh', really. Part of me has grown up similarly conservative. I think a lot more parents could be employing 'If in doubt, don't' these days. Hapless Gen Y and Z #dreamchasers are taught to 'Shoot for the stars, baby!' They're told they can achieve anything in life they set their minds to. It's heartbreaking for them when they find out they can't.

My default setting was: 'Expect nothing and be pleasantly surprised.' Addendum: 'Any pleasant surprise will be a massive fluke and should be dismissed as such.'

This is why you should take my account of childhood and run it through your own sunshiny filter, adding a leafy suburb here, an idyllic seaside holiday there, *The Morecambe and Wise Christmas Special* on the telly, and being read the adventures of Winnie the Pooh every bath night – because those things were there, too.

In my memory, it's like Nordic noir: everyone's withdrawn and secretive, the sky is overcast, and people drift about wearing thick woollen jumpers (Dad never turned on the central heating). At any moment someone's liable to walk out into a snowdrift and never return. But I am not the most reliable witness.

Nobody wants to start their own book looking like a sap, but the point of this chapter is to illustrate that childhood temperament is a strong predictor of problematic substance use in adulthood. Temperament is observable from birth, and it's the foundation upon which personality is built.

There's an episode of the 2012 ABC documentary *Life at Seven* called 'Tackling Temperament'. The Australian children it follows have been the subjects of a longitudinal study since birth, and now it's time to test their response to frustration with 'The Painting Experiment'.

In groups of three, the children in the documentary are given the task of painting a picture of flowers. Midway through they're distracted by a researcher, who calls them over to inspect the real floral arrangement more closely. While their backs are turned, one girl – who's in on the experiment – scribbles on their artwork, then slips back to her own easel.

Initially, each child is dismayed to discover their ruined painting – and they're suspicious, of course.

Child 1 is subdued. She says she knows the other girl did it, but she keeps going with her painting regardless. By the time she skips out of the room, the insult is forgotten.

Child 2 finds another blank page beneath the first and, pleased with his own ingenuity, starts over from scratch.

Child 3 wants to get to the bottom of it, but eventually her desire to continue wins out. 'I know,' she decides, 'I could colour the background in.'

Child 4 is angry. She stamps her foot. 'That just can't happen,' she says. The researcher leans in: so what should Child 4 do? 'I don't know,' she whimpers. Does she have an idea? 'No.' She rejects the suggestion of turning over the paper to the clean side, claiming that won't work.

'How did it happen?' Child 4 repeats, aghast. Eventually she's persuaded to start over, but the sense of injustice lingers.

Perhaps Child 4 adopted a permanent explanation for this ruined-painting scenario. This is a mindset described by psychologist Martin Seligman in his book *The Optimistic Child.* A positive thinker will regard a setback as being temporary: 'This picture has been ruined but at least I had only just started.' A child as pessimistic as I was will tell themselves a story with finality to it: 'This is hopeless. Just my luck. This happens every time. People always have it in for me.' This type will also have what's called an external locus of control: the belief that they are a passive victim of their circumstances, rather than the architect of their own destiny. Every time a reasonable solution is offered, they'll play the 'yes, but' game, preferring to nurse that sense of unfairness like Gollum and his ring. Something might go really well yet by the end of the day it's catastrophised, remembered as an unmitigated disaster. They might similarly revise their entire childhood, levelling out all experiences to the baseline of the worst.

That's the past. As for the future – which in Child 4's case is the option of turning over a sheet of paper and starting anew – they're harbingers of doom.

In defence of Child 4, certainly not all pessimistic or reactive children will grow up wanting to funnel the world up one nostril. There are plenty of coping techniques that, with a bit of encouragement, an individual can employ to regulate their moods. As my mum pointed out, upon reading this chapter, *she* was a pessimistic child and never sought solace in vodka. She does distract herself with lists, and lists of lists, and lists of lists of lists, though, which flutter like butterflies around the kitchen whenever someone opens the back door. And if one more person tells her, seemingly apropos of nothing, that she should try mindfulness, she's going to throttle them – and have another coffee.

The ruined paintings of the *Life at Seven* kids were a minor setback. In the case of experiencing childhood trauma, having low resilience – like Child 4 – can be a huge risk factor for adult anxiety, depression and problematic substance use.

One of the most thorough studies of childhood personality began in Melbourne in 1983 and is ongoing. The psychologists and paediatricians behind the Australian Temperament Project have been following the children of 2443 Victorian families. They've found that the features of temperament most likely to have long-term influence are persistence, flexibility and reactivity/emotionality, with the biggest predictor of adult behaviour being self-regulation.

Someone with poor self-regulation has little capacity to control their reactions, which include physiological responses, such as a churning stomach when something is upsetting, but also their interpersonal attitudes. I was one of those kids who, if a friend came over to play and a row started, would rather endure an hour of anvil-heavy, atom-buzzing silence until their mother arrived to take them away, than try to rectify the situation. Not much has changed. Fast-forward thirty years and there I am necking two beta-blockers before resigning from a job, in order to firmly get my points across without hurling a stapler or letting loose a spittled string of expletives.

The rage. The fucking rage! It's always there, inflating inside me, like the Hindenburg awaiting a match. I've no doubt that it was the fiery fuel of my benders for all those years, though I hid it well. Usually. Once, on a work trip to California, I thrashed a hotel room so soundly with my belt that the people in the room below – who'd probably already had it up to the hilt after a day at Disneyland with their actual kids – called front desk. The concierge wouldn't accept my explanation that I'd just had some annoying news and a few martinis, and pushed me aside to check the wardrobes and bathroom for my assailant.

So why do some people fail at self-regulation? In part it's hereditary, but it's also down to the home environment. When a child's stress-response systems are activated – which means an increased heart rate, rise in blood pressure and release of stress hormones – some calm intervention by a caregiver can bring these responses back down to baseline. If these skills are not observed and learned, the habit of self-regulation will not be routed into the neural pathways. Failure to learn might be through parental neglect or through watching parents catastrophise minor issues.

Conversely, pandering to a child's every whim can mean they'll never experience disappointment and how to adapt to it. Increasingly, drug and alcohol counsellors are seeing clients in their thirties and forties who are living back at home with enabling parents who never learned to tell them 'no'.

In summary, what we know to be high-risk factors for problematic substance use include low resilience, poor self-regulation, low self-efficacy and reactivity. These are all issues that can be tackled with cognitive behavioural therapy, or even with the assistance of the self-help section at any airport bookstore, with techniques put in place before you're back on the ground at your destination. The danger is that defeat can become comforting. There's a familiar cycle of disappointment and then – if you grow up to coddle yourself with drugs and alcohol – self-soothing. In time, defeat becomes a self-fulfilling prophecy. Things are not for the likes of you. Something simply cannot be done. There is no point.

The brain of a young child might as well be Play-Doh, such is its ability to be moulded. The most critical development period is between the ages of one and seven, but maturation takes form over a few decades, through the establishment of neural pathways.

These pathways are shaped by repeated behaviour – such as learning language and tootling away on the recorder – in the same way that taking the same route every day through the countryside will establish a track. Information travels down the pathways in the form of neurons, so the routes we create through our habits determine what kind of information we pay attention to.

But traumatic experiences and environmental factors such as family breakdown, unstable housing, poverty, and dysfunctional parenting can cause profound changes in the wiring of the developing brain. So can the erosive stress of racism, colonisation of your entire culture, or the kind of wartime childhood of my parents.

One of my father's earliest memories is of his bedroom window smashing in during the Blitz, showering his teddy bear with glass. His own dad dug bodies out of an East End school, in which 600 people had been sheltering before it scored a direct hit. He wound up spending two spells in a police sanatorium. My mother's family lived for some time under the misapprehension that her father had been lost at sea after his destroyer was sunk in battle. When he returned, my mother was reunited with a stranger; one who'd survived 115 crewmates.

It's hard for a Gen Xer like me, entrenched in an era of confessional navel-gazing, to imagine employing such a stiff upper lip. But to keep calm and carry on, as the wartime slogan goes, doesn't mean the art of resilience and self-regulation has been learned. More likely, wartime kids were just warned to keep quiet or else; their generation (1925–45) is even known as the Silent Generation.

Then there's intergenerational trauma, as experienced by the children of Holocaust survivors and of course Aboriginal families. Such trauma can induce epigenetic changes to sperm and egg cells through chemical tags that attach to our DNA, switching genes on and off, and increasing the likelihood of stress disorders in the next generation. In other words, stress is affecting the individual's brain before they've even been born, through fetal programming.

Addiction expert Dr Gabor Maté explained in his TEDxRio+20 talk, 'The Power of Addiction and the Addiction of Power', that he had been a baby when the German Army moved into Budapest. When the infant Maté wouldn't stop crying, his mother called the paediatrician, who explained that Jewish babies were crying en masse. 'Why?' adult Maté mused. 'What do babies know about Hitler or genocide or war? Nothing. What they're picking up on is the stresses, the terrors and the depression of our mothers. And that actually shapes the child's brain. What happens then is I get the message that the world doesn't want me. Because if she's not happy around me, she must not want me.' He concludes that this experience pushed him to become so renowned as a doctor that everybody would need him. 'This is how we pass it on. We pass on the trauma and suffering unconsciously from one generation to the next.'

The effect of this kind of early-life stress on the brain can serve an individual a double whammy. Rats, as ever, can demonstrate. In 2002, Professor Michael Meaney observed with his team that rats who had experienced maternal separation went on to have significantly higher responses to stress and higher sensitivity to cocaine. For humans, being sensitised to stress can lead to significant long-term neurophysiological adaptations, provoking intense anxiety, reactivity and hypervigilance, perhaps even triggering a range of psychiatric disorders. Then, if they self-soothe these symptoms with drugs, they'll have a heightened sensitivity to the effects and so will become highly motivated to continue taking them.

A person's physical health doesn't fare much better. Back in 1995, Dr Vincent Felitti, who was the director of an obesity clinic, and medical epidemiologist Dr Robert Anda began interviewing 17,000 participants in San Diego. This became the groundbreaking, longitudinal Adverse Childhood Experiences (ACE) Study that identified ten types of childhood trauma and examined the long-term health outcomes. The higher the number of adversities experienced, the more susceptible the participant was, not only to problematic substance use, promiscuity, depression and suicidal tendencies, but also to physical conditions such as obesity, decreased immune system efficiency, increased inflammatory response, heart disease, cancer and lung disease.

In comment sections across the internet, the battle rages eternal as to whether drug-takers are mad, bad or sad. The research is clear. A toxic combination of temperament traits and environmental stress efficiently turns some people into a time bomb for addiction.

Perhaps there's something else insidiously growing in that Petri dish of you. Child sexual abuse is an almost drearily familiar tale to those working in the drug and alcohol field. The professionals whom I interviewed for this book variously said that around seventy per cent to 'ninety-nine-point-nine' per cent of their female clients had been sexually abused as children. And yet politicians persist in investing their energies into the war on drugs rather than tackling addiction as a public health issue.

I had a cock in my mouth by the age of seven. It was fairly pedestrian abuse when set against some of the stories I've heard in researching this book, but it set off a catastrophic chain reaction all the same.

It was a neighbourhood boy, five years older and a big lug, with a bumfluff moustache and the sullen countenance of Adrian Mole. Adrian had known me since I was born. It was during a game of sardines that we found ourselves behind the same patchwork curtain. He reckoned I'd groped him, and he announced it loudly. I hadn't, but I laughed like a donkey, delighted to be included in older company.

The game disintegrated, but after I'd gone to bed he took the stairs stealthily and woke me up. There was such a struggle to prise my hands away from between my legs that, to this day, I have a phobia of being touched on the hollows of my hips where he dug in with his fingers, even if it's just a cat jumping on my lap.

'You shouldn't be doing this,' he whispered admiringly, between smothering wet kisses that patiently sought out my mouth whenever I whipped my head away into the pillow. His subsequent visits grew more daring. It took me about fifteen years to sleep well again.

The thought of telling my mother about Adrian was so agonising that, when I finally did, I underplayed the details, not that I would have had the vocabulary to elaborate. He had been coming to my room and ... *meaningful look*. I thought the hint had been taken, a misunderstanding that dragged out for decades, but actually he'd been mistaken for a pest, not a sex pest. Adrian was allowed to keep coming over. Having been ordered not to disturb me at night, he instead bored his eyes into me over the dinner table, or covertly reached for my hand in the car.

On the surface, life carried on as normal. I wrote a newspaper on my typewriter and distributed it, in rollerskates, on our street.

I learned recorder and became absorbed in the maths of music. I built a Barbie house out of a cardboard box and Dad's fag packets. I familiarised myself with the oeuvre of Andrew Lloyd-Webber and Tim Rice. Watched by a shelf of Cabbage Patch Kids, I taught a friend how to have oral sex until she whined at me to stop. She tasted like the gap behind a loose milk tooth.

But weird things were happening in class. I'd be trying to pay attention to the teacher and the top of my skull would rise up into a burning hot ridge. I had to keep patting it. Sometimes the burning would spread downwards to my old chickenpox scar, and I'd dig my nails into that. My fingers would trace the trail of lava, over my lips, down the centre of my throat, down my sternum. At night, I had to chant an increasingly long chain of farewells to my mother before she was allowed to leave the room, all in the right order. In the morning, my teeth ached from grinding. When I walked to school, I'd keep tapping the sign of the cross on my chest, relieved by its symmetry.

My best friend – my kindred spirit, as Anne of Green Gables would say – was cast out from our group in my cruel, prolonged bullying campaign. We'd always insisted we were the same in every way. Now we were not, and I resented her with a simmering spite that wouldn't abate. A girl from over the road told her parents about a sexual dance I'd been doing (in all fairness, I was choreographing a Bananarama song) and she wasn't allowed to come over anymore. A boy who lived around the corner agreed to push a screwdriver handle up inside me, then we took turns pissing behind a hedge. That was becoming a bit of a theme. Sometimes, alone, I would pee on the bedroom carpet. I didn't know why.

But for three years I never thought about Adrian. Then, when I was ten, I remembered that summer as if I was emerging from a blackout. I'd been doing as the Brownie Guide Handbook had advised: trying to clean the house before my parents awoke, so that they would be thrilled with their secret helper. Who could it be? They'd never know. A Brownie Guide never curries favour.

I wasn't really being as selfless as an elf, because I was opening the kitchen cupboard to retrieve the vacuum cleaner, the noise of which would alert sleeping parents to any pious activity. I reached for it and I remembered everything. Triggered by what? Seemingly nothing. But the guilt and shame washed over me like a stain that would never come out.

My family were atheists, but I started going to church alone, searching for comfort and hoping that God, the ultimate judge of character, would let me know I was off the hook. The shame of re-enacting Adrian's scenes with friends my own age made me feel complicit. I had a children's Bible with an index at the back, which was supposed to list your potential concern and then refer you to an appropriate passage, but they didn't have anything about oral sex. Maybe it was the wrong denomination. Anyhow, when comfort never came, I renounced the Lord. A persistent rage began to burn in my heart.

At home I was alternately clingy and distant. I became hypervigilant to the sexual interest of men around me, which, now the scales had fallen from my eyes, seemed omnipresent and insidious. When it was there, I felt revulsion. When it wasn't there, I tried to incite it. Eight, nine, ten years old: flouncing past men drinking cider in a graveyard and getting a thrill when one of them muttered,

'I would if I was older'; making eyes at soldiers in a troopy on the motorway out of the back window of our family car; rolling around on the floor when someone came to the door to talk to my mother.

Like most young girls in the 1980s, I'd been heavily into Wham! – the pop duo whose tight shorts, peppy backing singers and sloganeering T-shirts were designed to illuminate the circuits of the prepubescent brain. But post-Adrian, I became repelled by George Michael. The two had the same flicky fringe, square face and slant of the eyes. Thirty years on, if I see someone's eyebrow hairs flaring towards the middle, or hear a whiny nasal admonishment, or see a petulant lower lip that might stick to mine – just these minute traces – I recoil. Sometimes I even spot them fleetingly in myself and am revolted.

Already this dichotomy was developing: rage and need, two sides of a coin. If I was sure nobody could hear, I'd pummel the soft furnishings, threaten the walls, splinter pencils in my mouth. Among my harem of dolls there was one plastic-haired boy. One afternoon I punched him till his eyelids rattled. I obliterated his face with crayons, stabbed him with a kitchen knife, and left him for dead in a flowerbed.

While the Australian Temperament Project found no differences between boys and girls concerning anxiety, the findings *did* support the idea of girls having higher levels of depression than boys, from the age of thirteen onwards.

Anhedonia is a symptom of depression in which the individual has a reduced capacity to feel pleasure. It can be triggered by rodeo-riding the reward circuits, but it can also occur through being stuck in an environment without any control (be that at home, school or prison), which begets no stimulation of the reward system. The cruel irony is that someone might use drugs to lift them out of the sort of teenage anhedonia that can come about through circumstances, then emerge the other end, decades later, in a version that's drug-induced.

In the 1970s psychiatrist Aaron Beck defined 'the cognitive triad'. Essentially, people who are depressed believe that the self is powerless, the world is unfair, and the future is unchanging. But while someone so inclined might think there's no point in trying to facilitate change, there's always the option of self-soothing. That's where drugs come in.

'Have a banana,' Mum would say routinely, once I hit thirteen and anhedonia hit me back. She'd read that bananas would boost serotonin levels, which would surely help my mood. (We know better now, though: serotonin derived from bananas can't cross the blood–brain barrier.)

I needed something stronger than a banana. I'd found that lately I was avoiding my classmates during school time and dragging myself around my usual high-street haunts at weekends, sapped of all energy. I couldn't figure out what was wrong with me. I wasn't from a broken home, and that's where my imagination ran out. There was a hard lump in my throat, a keening sensation in my chest, and what felt like a vice clamped around my forehead.

Slough is anhedonia-made-concrete. Back in the late 1980s the central strip had 'Murder Park' at one end and the greyhound stadium at the other. Somewhere in the middle was A Classy

Touch, which did thickshakes popular with kids. It's since been crowded out by chain pubs doing three-for-one alcopop deals.

Every day on the way to school I walked past a massive cock and balls spray-painted on a fence that seemed to have been there all my life (but it was probably more like a decade, given the Siouxsie and the Banshees graffiti next to it). Women were represented, too – graffiti in the local playground had punchlines about the Billingsgate Fish Market. The swings would frequently be hurled up and around the frame, tangled out of reach. The slide wore a long smear of dog shit. In my memory, the swimming pool (opposite Murder Park) had a ubiquitous pervert squatting behind goggles at the end of every lane.

Of course I'm being true to type by remembering Slough in a dim light, instead of, say, recalling how great the pound shops were (and, indeed, still are). I negotiated those pound shops like a deaf mute, experimenting with how long I could go without talking. I could still muster the energy to scream at my mother from time to time. 'Spitting blood,' Dad called it, with detached curiosity.

During my childhood I'd noted my mysterious father coming in late from work in London and heading straight for the lounge room. My eyes would be fixed on the TV screen, but my own antenna was angled to the back of the room. I'd hear the scrape of the heavy tumbler being drawn from the shelf, the click of the key rotating in the lock, the clank of one bottle against another and the bock-bock-bock of the whisky being decanted.

Something was lying dormant within me, waiting for a trigger. It came one afternoon when my mother picked me up outside the swimming pool. In the car, she told me that Dad's mother had died. I hadn't been close to my grandmother and I was unsure how to feel or act. Something was expected of me and I didn't have the goods. More than that, I sensed that I had been handed a hall pass, an excuse to react.

With my parents holed up in separate corners of the house, I headed for the lounge room and turned the TV up high. The drinks cabinet smelled of wood varnish and barrel-aged spirits; a blend that persists in my memory. I took a tumbler and poured a bit of everything into it – port, sherry, whisky, something foreign and unpronounceable – until the glass was full. Just inhaling it raised the hair on my arms and lit up some dim region of my brain. The scorch in my throat was a jolt to the heart after months of flatlining. 'I am here,' it announced.

For many, the equation is simple. Drugs and alcohol are pain-killers. The pain that is felt might be emotional, but it's still the anterior cingulate cortex – the area of the brain that responds to physical pain – that agitates the vagus nerve connecting the brain stem to the chest and the abdomen, manifesting distress as real pain in these regions. A handful of studies since 2010 have even concluded that emotional pain and rejection can be alleviated with paracetamol.

Whether a person takes paracetamol or heroin to alleviate their emotional pain, they are delaying moving through the cognitive stages that are needed to process trauma. That kind of work takes time, energy, self-awareness and guidance. For someone in urgent pain, substances are the path of least resistance.

A month after first opening the drinks cabinet, I'd crept back over and over, and discovered Pernod, Southern Comfort and

Jameson. Now I knew their names and we'd formed a tight bond, curtains drawn, TV low. I glossed over the fact that after a couple of hours of drinking I'd hiss abuse at myself in the bathroom mirror and rake my arms with coat hangers. While still in the heady moments of the first hour or so, I'd stand in the kitchen and talk to my ghost self in the reflection of the window, haloed and pale under the strip light as the whisky sang its background chorus. 'Remember this girl,' I told myself one day, imprinting the image in my brain. 'Don't forget her.'

We both turned at the sound of an engine. It was my father's car in the drive – too early. I ran back into the lounge room, to the satanic circle of bottles in which I had sat earlier. I had time only to roll the booze bounty under the sofa, then take the stairs in twos. As Dad pushed open the front door, I gathered spare socks, my ATM card, my school bag, and assumed the sprinting position. By now, I'd definitely inherited the trait of avoiding discussion.

I heard him turn the key of the empty cabinet. A pause. Dad cleared his throat and went into the back garden, giving me time to return to the scene of the crime and rehome the bottles. By the time he'd hosed the garden, I was back in my room. I'd got away with it. The art of having a double life became engrained in my psyche, and over the years became a guilty pleasure, even for something as simple as having a slug of vodka in the toilets then returning to resume a conversation.

Very soon I felt my DNA intertwining with alcohol, like Seth Brundle and the Fly. Hungry for information, I took out library books on drugs. Uppers. Downers. Psychedelics. A world of possibilities stretched out in front of me. *You mean to say that if I take this little pill, just like Alice in Wonderland I will change entirely?* It was an irresistible offer to someone who wanted everything to change, but mostly themselves.

As my personality took shape, I built an internal narrative around my beliefs, and that narrative scored pathways through my brain: mainly, that I was the pariah of the family and should quarantine myself, which brought with it resentment. Anything that served to confirm this narrative over the next few years gave me an odd sense of triumph. I might not tell people about the abuse but, nevertheless, I had my excuse to behave as I saw fit. I kept my hall pass close.

2

BABY MISOGYNIST

Hitching identity to drink, drugs and men

I was born onto the losing team. I tried to keep that under wraps for as long as I could, but come puberty all my careful constructions of being one of the blokes scattered like dust.

Being born a girl was an accelerant poured on the embers of my rage. As I saw it, the women in our family were second-class citizens; literally, if you count the time Dad flew business and left Mum in economy. On holidays as a family, we'd troop behind Dad like ducklings. He'd saunter from restaurant to restaurant, rubbing his stubble as he perused the menu boards. We may have waited docilely for the executive decision, but I was mentally carving out that niche for myself.

On shorter trips to Essex to visit the paternal grandparents, I'd watch two generations of women at once be ridiculed over the Sunday roast by the men. Dad, in particular, had an intimidating intellect. He'd won a scholarship to Cambridge University in the 1960s, and I never quite outgrew the childish notion that he knew the answer to everything and could silence you as such.

I vowed to talk around men as economically as possible – which, in any case, was a manly thing to do. Women were silly and inconsequential, I could see that. On Saturday night TV they were either disposed of in a fetishistic manner, or they'd get in the way of Harrison Ford.

Dad's lifestyle was infinitely more appealing to me than Mum's, though that can in part be attributed to its mystery. When he wasn't working in London and taking long routes home, he was jetting off around the world, disappearing in cabs before I'd woken up, and reappearing with exotic gifts from every continent. The reality may have been more of (weirdly lengthy) conferences and bland hotel rooms, but I imagined him to be an international playboy. He looked very Warren Beatty or maybe like a young Clint Eastwood. When not in a suit, he got about in tighty-tight shorts, tennis socks, and shirts that were always falling open. He wore a large signet ring on his pinkie. No wedding ring, because it got in the way. Of the signet ring.

In his absence, I clicked through the hangers of his wardrobe. Each suit bore a fading embrace of aftershave, cigarette smoke and whisky. I'd try on the fur ushanka and the black leather jacket, then put them back carefully. On the shelf above was a neat stack of men's magazines that I would spend hours perusing of an afternoon, lying on the bed and swinging my stockinged feet. For the record, somebody does read the articles in those magazines, and it's a twelve-year-old girl in Slough.

The women in the photo spreads all had dusky furls of pubic hair and grains of sand clinging to their tawny thighs. Years later I'd work for adult magazines myself, as a subeditor, and would write fictional interviews with such models ('wind the aggression back a bit,' the editor would say), but for now I was more interested in the mechanics of sex. Over the course of a week, I called all the numbers in the adverts at the back of one magazine and listened to the recorded messages, but my literal interpretations of the metaphors had me stumped. I could stay on the phone for half an hour, the receiver pressed so tightly to my ear as to leave an imprint, and all I'd hear about were shafts and spray, on some vessel that went nowhere. Where was the sex?

Months later, Mum stormed into my bedroom brandishing a phone bill, upon which scores of familiar-looking premium-rate numbers were piled up.

'Did you call these?'

'No,' I said, barely looking up from my homework.

'Right,' she said, tight-lipped. 'That's all I needed to know.'

I doubt anything came of my fib. It was rare that Dad was in trouble with Mum, because she and I took our womanly frustrations out on each other, at top volume. She didn't deserve that. Mum went out to work, chauffeured me to character-building activities, and took on the burdens of friends and family. She doggedly ploughed her way through a GCSE, an A-level and a degree, turning my brother's old bedroom into a tiny study, crammed with books, maps and artefacts. I'd call her 'Martyr Mummy', for daring to tell us she was at the end of her tether. *Do as Dad does, then*, I thought. Whatever that was. I was sure about one thing: men got away with everything, while women were held accountable for themselves and everyone else.

My solution was to get all Rex Harrison on womankind.

I congratulated myself whenever I thought like a man, in a terse, unemotional way. I'd stroke my chin contemplatively and sit askew in my jeans, which I paired with a grey Levi's sweatshirt. This was the uniform of boy gangs eternal; in *The Outsiders, Rumble Fish, Stand by Me, The Goonies*; way preferable to the paperback sororities of *The Baby-Sitters Club* and *Sweet Valley High*. The ultimate boy gangs were bands. I listened to heavy metal by osmosis, absorbing my older brother's records through the wall and pinching his copies of *Kerrang!* in order to memorise every word. With an encyclopaedic knowledge of the genre might also come acceptance.

Women had but one role in heavy metal: to under-dress in corsets and stockings. I saw no wrong in a band posing with topless groupies, manipulating breasts like they were balloon animals. It was pantomime; you could take it no more seriously than you took Manowar wearing loincloths. I knew that, if I were to walk into a dressing-room in my black jeans and denim jacket with studs and patches, the band would hit pause on the cavorting and look upon me with admiration and respect. *You*, they'd think, *you're different*, as they handed me a bottle of bourbon. I associated alcohol with the winning team; it represented freedom.

Yet in interviews, these blokes had a tendency to say things like: 'Show me a creative woman and I'll show you a barren woman' or 'Women look ridiculous playing guitars' or 'We chose a female support band so we could have more options' or 'Any girl over the age of fourteen and still a virgin is a pain in the crack.' So I might have been striving to be the biggest misogynist of them all, but I couldn't ignore the fact that my role was simply to be a good sport. Later still, the penny would drop that to hate my gender was to hate myself.

Thank god for my heavy-metal-endorsed buddies, Jack Daniels and Jim Beam.

The spunky kid I used to be had wasted away with a consumptive cough as soon as I hit puberty. Now I was a floating amoeba without discernible form or feature.

Like something out of *Invasion of the Body Snatchers*, my girl peers had matured in the break between primary school and high school and emerged fully indoctrinated into the new regime: that we must trade adventure, possibility, and fantasy in our lunch-breaks for sitting inert against the science lab wall, blowing smoke rings. In another year, we'd be expected to start barging the new intake in the corridor and calling them slags. I didn't speak this language at all. Beneath my antisocial fringe hid a kid who spent her summer holidays fishing flies out of a swimming pool, and school recess rescuing worms from the bitumen. I needed to construct a tougher personality, brick by brick.

But at what cost? Dr Genevieve Dingle from the University of Queensland tells me, 'When a person becomes engaged with substance use as a teenager, it's reasonable to assume that they will have less opportunity to develop the other aspects of their identity, such as those related to relationships, education, sport, art and other pursuits.'

Dingle's research has expanded on the prominent narrative in addiction literature: that a person loses their identity when becoming dependent on substances, then rediscovers it during recovery. Interviewing adults in treatment in 2015, her team found two identity-related pathways; one of loss, but the other of gain, particularly in socially isolated individuals who viewed addiction as a 'new valued social identity'. Of the women interviewed, a drug-related identity often helped them deal with feelings of social dislocation. This fits with other research that reveals that teenage girls often become the go-betweens of dealers and friends, in an effort to be the social glue of their little community.

Alcohol helped me, by lowering my inhibitions enough to raise my confidence. There's a flaw to that logic, though: if you convince yourself that alcohol makes you brave or aggressive, you will also convince yourself that it will be the next swig … no, the next … no, the next, that will make you precisely confident enough. We think of alcohol as being a social lubricant, but it can equally buffer the loner from the outside world.

In the back of *Kerrang!* I found girl penpals with long fringes, all harbouring their own gothic tales of isolation. While our peers hung out at shopping centres, we spent our Saturdays sketching the labels of bottles of fortified wine. (Not only does fortified wine fortify the defences on a budget, but its best-known brands – Thunderbird and Night Train – have been immortalised in song by everyone from Townes Van Zandt to Guns N' Roses to the Beastie Boys.)

So that was toughness sorted, thanks to booze. Now to be interesting: drugs. Drugs have been making awkward people look dark and mysterious since time immemorial. Formulating my narcotic persona became a single-minded pursuit. I read the usual suspects – Leary, Wolfe, Kesey, Burroughs, Thompson – all men, of course. I listened to the trippers – Zappa, Captain Beefheart, Bongwater – and swapped intel with like-minded souls.

Back in 1974, Harvard psychiatrist Edward Khantzian hypothesised that people use drugs to compensate for deficient ego function. Drugs, he suggested, are an 'ego solvent'. In 2012 he wrote that sedatives, in particular: 'can dissolve defences against otherwise threatening connection to others ... and stimulants can break through the inertia and inhibitions that do not allow contact with other human beings.'

My *Kerrang!* friends and I bolstered our shoddy self-esteem by writing ten-page accounts of our dreams of going postal, on Basildon Bond paper from our mothers. Talking of postal, we soon established a drug ring through Royal Mail, swapping acid and speed, which I wedged behind the posters of my bedroom, secured by pins.

It was amyl nitrate – or 'poppers' – that became my new security blanket, clanking away in my army satchel alongside the quarter-bottle of vodka. When sniffed, poppers gave you an almost unbearable head rush, drained the bloom from your cheeks to leave a clammy curd, and reduced you to giggles. Timed with setting the needle down on a record, it made music a million times more meaningful. Oh, the joy of peeling the gold casing off a dinky bottle and lifting it to its maiden voyage.

I first discovered poppers when I took the coach up to Nottingham to visit one penpal, Karen, who took me on a tour of the fetish shops that stocked it. Liquid Gold, Bang Aroma, TNT.

Karen lived with her mother and stepfather in a two-up two-down. That first night, as we got ready to go out and meet her Axl Rose–modelled boyfriend, she lit a joss stick and we took a solemn sniff of the poppers she kept in a box under the bed. There was a photo of her real father in there, and my letters. Her mother never bothered snooping, she said.

Karen told me about life trapped in a house with her stepfather. He'd stopped molesting her when she turned twelve, but every now and then he still offered her ten pounds to sit on his lap. She shrugged at me; her sweet face expressionless under a curtain of hennaed hair. 'I might as well get a tenner for it.'

That night, we went out to Rock City and sniffed poppers and danced for hours, until I slipped in a puddle of snakebite-and-black and split my chin open on a goth's boot spur.

Back in Slough, I soon got about with scabbed nostrils, trailed by a distinctive smell that had my mother sniffing theatrically whenever I walked in the room. At school, I coached people to dip their cigarettes in a bottle of amyl for a next-gen smoking experience, and became known – to my intense pleasure – as 'Junkie Jen'. (Ten years later a co-worker at the porn mags would give me the superhero name 'Nicotina Staines'. By then, it felt like less of a triumph.)

My new identity could be described as 'everything to prove' or, perhaps, 'protesting too much', but at least I had one – and additionally, I now had a reputation. I graduated with honours when I was fourteen and took the coach up to Birmingham to see my brother, who was at university there. It was the day after I'd crashed Mum's car, which his housemates had already heard about. *Then* I introduced them to the joys of amyl nitrate. The admiration in their eyes as they staggered about the dance floor at the student union indie disco was beautiful to behold. I was a legend among men.

I was hitching my identity to drink and drugs – and to men. The very fact that I liked drink and drugs at all typecast me as a ladette, the spare rib of the 1990s lad. Apparently it's a man's world; we just drink in it.

The media has a habit of identifying genres of female imbibers, as though women who drink and take drugs are some cartoonish anomaly. The labels simply change to suit the culture of the times, from the good-time girls of the 1940s (platinum blondes who run off with jazz drummers), to the party girls of the 2000s (blondes who overdose on pills at festivals).

'Ladette' was a label slapped on young, gobby women, most prominently those working in TV and radio in the UK – such as Sara Cox and Zoe Ball – who smashed pints like they were starting a fight and weren't backwards in coming forwards. Really, it was just the media's update of the 1980s 'wild child' – posh totty such as Amanda de Cadenet, Tottie Goldsmith and Mandy Smith, who swigged champagne while dancing on tables in their undergarments as the paparazzi panted beneath them.

The ladette flailed on until 2010, partly due to the UK and Australian versions of the TV show *From Ladette to Lady*. These days, study of the species is limited to where-are-they-now stories of redemption or disgrace. In 2015, Sara Cox won paternalistic approval from *The Telegraph* UK for having 'cleaned up her act'. The headline ran: 'I'm partial to an early night in my jammies.' By contrast, Zoe Ball has been cast by the *Daily Mail* as the tragi-pathetic fallen woman whose unbecoming boozing has led to the divorce court. The tabloid throws stones at her, then tells us how to get her look.

Even for those ladettes who came 'good', it's possible there's a health legacy. Research from the Glasgow Centre for Population Health compared the death rates from liver disease, hepatitis and other alcohol-related damage for men and women from Liverpool, Manchester and Glasgow who were born between 1910 and 1979. They found that death rates spiked dramatically in women born in the 1970s, who came of age in the ladette era.

This can in part be attributed to changing attitudes about women drinking – consider that in Queensland in the 1960s, women weren't even allowed into bars, and elsewhere they were relegated to the ladies' lounge. However, it also coincides with the launch of sunny alcopops in the late 1980s, marketed at teenage girls not yet accustomed to the man-sized taste of beer. The funny thing was, alcopops tended to have a much higher alcohol-by-volume, often at around six-and-a-half per cent to lager's four per cent. I can't help picturing snickering marketing execs bandying around potential slogans: 'goes down easy'; 'doesn't taste as bad as you think'. In any case, they wouldn't be the first to equate cheap fizz to being a 'leg opener'. Back in the early 1980s, Wolf Blass even named one of his sparkling wines 'René Pogel'. Sounds well classy, till you read it backwards.

For a woman who heartily enjoys sex, or compulsively seeks it out for other reasons, booze can be a handy tool in absolving her of all responsibility. Handy, since the playing field still isn't level when it comes to society's view of sexually active men and women. Not so handy because, while alcohol lowers inhibition, it also kills libido by dulling sensitivity.

Alcopops found their spiritual home on reality TV shows such as *Geordie Shore*, provided by producers to facilitate the level of drunkenness required to make young folk copulate on national telly. There's an illusion of power in being as sexually aggressive as men are allowed to be, but it can sometimes take a stupefying blood-alcohol level to override the misgivings. Young women have sexual allure but very little agency, which can move them to construct a hypersexual identity.

The painful conflict between two opposing ideas or values within the mind is called cognitive dissonance. As a form of psychological stress, cognitive dissonance is often a driver of problematic substance use. While further down the track that might literally come down to 'to score or not to score – I shouldn't get high, but I want to', it's common to begin in a more existential way in adolescence. Picture the kid trying to be loyal to both parents after a divorce. Or the kid trying to deny the colour of their skin. Or the kid trying to hide their sexuality, perhaps even from themselves.

According to Australia's National Drug Strategy Household Survey of 2013, gay and bisexual people are nearly six times more likely to use ecstasy than heterosexual people, and are over four times more likely to use meth. Beyond Blue produced a fact sheet on depression and anxiety in LGBTQI people that reveals that non-heterosexual women are more than three times as likely to have generalised anxiety disorder than heterosexual women.

The issues for trans people are even more complex. Matt Tilley is a clinical professional fellow at Curtin University's Department of Sexology. He's one of the researchers behind the First Australian National Trans Mental Health Study, released in 2014. Nine hundred and forty-six respondents took part, making it the third-largest international study on trans mental health in the world.

'We found that trans people were four times as likely to have ever been diagnosed with depression, and approximately one-and-a-half times as likely to have ever been diagnosed with anxiety,' Tilley says. Unsurprisingly, then, twenty-six per cent of respondents who identified as trans women, and twenty-one per cent who identified as being assigned male at birth or non-binary, reported having used an illicit drug. That's substantially higher than the figure for the Australian population in general, which – according to the 2010 National Drug Strategy Household Survey – is fifteen per cent. Drugs, after all, offer not only comfort, but total acceptance.

Brisbane-born, Toronto-based Sunny Drake is a theatre performer and producer who came out as a trans man when he was twenty-nine and gave up the booze six years later. His show *X* drew on more than forty interviews he conducted with queer and trans people on the topic of addiction.

'For a long time, drinking was about dampening a part of me that couldn't be expressed,' he tells me of the habit that began when he was a teenage girl. He's heard many stories of kids in his position who layered on the bravado. 'Being a teenager is just fucking hard anyway, but when you have to bury a part of yourself to cope in a context where there's no room for you, you grow up in a cultural void. I had to create a large void in myself in which to tuck away my identity. And then I needed something else to fill the rest of that void.'

I could recognise that conflict over identity from my own teenage years. Only, in my case, the cognitive dissonance came through the belief that I'd be better off being a bloke. It conflicted with the knowledge that I could only really sleep with them.

At seventeen, I came up with my own super-turbo persona and committed it to paper. Actually, in my self-published magazine, *Slapper: The Groupie's Guide to Gropable Bands*, I had many pseudonyms, as though trying to spread out the blame.

These characters ran amok, as did I, through the venues and hotels of London. It was true that I only interviewed bands that I found attractive in their promo photos – my prerogative – but the groupie thing was chiefly an angle. I had great ambitions as a writer. There were a million fanzines out there, and mine needed a hook. Armed with glue and a guillotine, I churned *Slapper* out with different themes, such as the Obsessive Fan issue and the (pun intended) Daddy issue. Rules: no earnest, sycophantic stuff.

At weekends I bought clip-art books of foxy ladies from a niche shop in Covent Garden, and delivered more issues to Tower Records and Rough Trade. Stylistically, I seesawed between misogynist and misandrist, reading Valerie Solanas'

SCUM Manifesto alongside the classic sexists – Bukowski, Roth, Amis, Mailer, Updike, Hemingway, Kerouac. I determined to out-aggro them all, though my prose was lifted directly from *A Clockwork Orange*.

There were accounts of run-ins with riot grrrls and publicists, tips on how to stalk rock stars, and reviews of hotel-room amenities. I'd tot up how much the record company spent on me in drinks and food and run the tally throughout the interviews, and advise other budding writers on what shops offered the best prices for those unwanted promo CDs. Bands with the bad luck of having an over-eager publicist hooking them up with any and every interview opportunity found themselves at the business end of my massive tape recorder. My interrogations were usually carried out in an alcoholic stupor, such was my shyness, and usually took the form either of psychological evaluation, or of deliberately annoying questions. I'd print the ensuing disaster verbatim. These interviews came to capture my new identity, really: a defiant 'well, what are you going to do about it?'

The old desire to be part of the boy gang had found its natural home with *Slapper*. I couldn't be them, but by sleeping with them I absorbed them. In that spirit, I called one instalment the Cannibalistic Groupie issue.

Still, *Slapper* presented yet another uncomfortable dichotomy. On the one hand, I had a relentless interest in sex and the power dynamic around it. On the other hand, my very male desire to hunt down and collect specific bedfellows was construed by the general public – the bedfellows included – as being degrading to women. Why wasn't I allowed to just enjoy my victories?

My identity as a hard-drinking, promiscuous hard-arse was well-and-truly sealed when the papers got wind of *Slapper*, and then I was saddled with it for years. I'd sent my work to an *NME* journalist whose amphetamine-fuelled alliteration I admired, hoping he would hold me aloft and introduce me as his protégé.

Slapper was doing okay, being distributed through Tower Records in the US, and stocked in all my favourite record shops in England, but it would have taken somebody with considerably more nous than I to steer it away from total disaster once this *NME* journalist thought outside the box and profiled me in the *Sunday Observer* as one of a new, utterly fictional trend of middle-class groupies.

'Why's Mum crying in the rose bushes?' my brother asked, on his visit home from uni. He stood perplexed at my bedroom door as I scoured the story, newspaper spread out on my floor. My initial hilarity had gradually been overtaken by something more anxious, and the bad feeling intensified as I read the headline one more time. *More sex, please, we're groupies – and proud of it!*

The crux of the piece – in well-formed quotes that simply couldn't have come out of my mouth – was that I was spearheading a new wave of stage-door botherers. As if! I always travelled alone. The picture was equally damning: me sprawled in my fishnets, my *Tank Girl* fringe coincidentally peaking into devil horns.

Dad paid my bedroom a rare visit and cleared his throat. 'You've really shafted your mother this time,' he said in his most business-like voice. We left it at that. Two hours later, Mum returned from an outing and opened the boot of her car like a Louis Vuitton handbag hawker on Slough High Street. She turfed out eighty copies of the *Sunday Observer*, hauled in over a four-mile radius.

Over the next few months I received endless requests for interviews. On the occasions I agreed – in order to set the record straight that I was merely a young journalist enjoying the perks of the job – I only made things worse. When I declined, I was used in braying beat-ups all the same. One magazine invited debate on my sluttiness. A newspaper ran a photo of a demure young lady in a tunic on the cover of its supplement, with the line: 'Spot the groupie: vice girl or nice girl?' In total, the big misunderstanding spread to three tabloids, eight broadsheets, eleven magazines, six radio programs and twelve TV chat shows, debates or documentaries, all of whom sent me interview requests but few of which I accepted.

By now I was getting self-pitying. While I wasn't leading a dignified life, I was way too drunk to be doing all the things people implied, and any record-label publicist worth her salt would be getting more sexy band action than I was. Yet those very same publicists were now gleefully putting me down on every guest list as 'Jenny Slapper'.

It was all supposed to be a big joke, but now the joke was on me. My identity had been well and truly defined.

3

CHAOS THEORY

Impulsivity, and how it escapes detection in teenage girls

Once, at primary school, everyone in my class was given a sheet of paper and told to follow the instructions. The first instruction was to read to the bottom of the paper before beginning. I ignored this and carried out each subsequent instruction as I read it, revelling in my reputation as the class's speediest reader. *Clap your hands. Stand up. Shout 'I am halfway through!'* Oh, the triumph of being first. Then, of course, you get to the final instruction and it tells you to ignore all the previous instructions and sit quietly.

This test is still fairly common in schools, designed to highlight the drawbacks of acting impulsively and demonstrate the value in taking care, particularly around exam time. The problem is, it takes impulsive people far longer to learn life lessons than it does others.

We're all on the spectrum of impulsivity somewhere, but having poor control is a big risk for problematic substance use. A quick note here on the difference between impulsivity and compulsivity, since problematic substance use can be an outcome of either or both. They're both independent dimensions that we all vary on, and those dimensions will have some overlap in terms of our inhibitory control. Compulsivity is characterised by intrusive thoughts and ritualistic, repetitive actions that bring some relief to anxiety, including drinking or taking drugs. Impulsivity tends to drive pleasurable, high-risk behaviours that are ill-thought out and prematurely expressed without regard for consequences.

In adolescence that terrible sense of urgency can be attributed in part to the new rush of sex hormones, prompting a desire to tick off every new experience with the conviction that a window of opportunity will slam shut at any minute. Plus, it's the areas of the brain that control impulses and planning ahead that are among the last to mature. But for some individuals, impulsivity is a dominant personality trait that rules, chaotically, into adulthood.

I had no idea how to behave as a teenager, and I was a teenager until I was thirty-four. Being staggeringly drunk all the time when you're young and irritating is a bit like affixing a bumper sticker to your fender that reads: *ASK ME HOW I AM.* Problem is, nobody wants to get close enough to read it. The things I blurted out had a tendency to make people angle away slightly, demand an explanation, or laugh – but not *with* me, you understand. My solution was to turn inappropriateness into my schtick but, really, I was wondering how everyone else seemed to have the manual for social etiquette.

A theme tune emerged for me: 'Embarrassment' by Madness. My brother is five years older, so his bedroom door was always shut. I'd lie outside the barricade, legs dangling down the stairs, and listen to the music emerging under the crack. Among his record collection was this seven-inch in which singer Suggs chastises someone for being a disgrace to the human race, punctuated by a furious sax solo. It's actually about the sax player's sister and her teenage pregnancy to a black man, which incurred shaming from some family members, but as a general accusation perhaps it explained why my brother always had an elastic band aimed at my head. And I hadn't really started hitting on all his friends yet.

At school I was constantly getting in strife with gangs of older kids, thanks to my inflammatory comebacks to their routine harassment of the year below. Paul Kelly's protagonist in 'Dumb Things' laments that he thought his friends would rush to his defence. I, too, would look around and my own gang would have dissipated. Each incident and accident would escalate into an exhausting, all-out vendetta that, having painted that target on my head, I'd have to commit to. I'd remain defiant against being shoved into walls, having my PE kit dumped into the toilet or being written about on classroom walls, but I was racking my brain the whole time: How could someone supposedly smart be so dumb?

The smart thing was a sore point, because in primary school I was regularly pulled out of class for aptitude tests and day-long workshops for the extraordinarily gifted. Oh, the smugness of being summoned from class, then returning hours later with a name sticker on my jumper, casually brushing off the questions.

After a few years of this I believed myself to be touched by the hand of greatness; destined for prizes, groundbreaking discoveries and first contact with other galaxies. I felt invincible.

That was good, that feeling. I'd kill for it now. It instilled in me a sense of otherness and made me fiercely competitive – another feeling I *loved*. The reality was I was innumerate and unable to concentrate on subjects that didn't interest me. Primary school, with its creative projects and emphasis on language, was a doddle, but once I started at a science-oriented grammar school at which we were expected to simply receive information, my grades slipped from this-child-must-be-some-kind-of-genius to middle-stream mundanity. I stopped trying, barely scraping into university.

People who get frustrated and give up quickly have what's called low self-efficacy, which is the strength of belief we have that we can achieve our goals. To put that in an addiction framework, they're likely to have low confidence in their ability to turn down a drink or a drug when offered. In terms of treatment outcome, if you don't believe you can resist a substance, you're more likely to have a lapse. Impulsive individuals are more likely to form exaggerated beliefs about how rewarding substances are, or how they need them to function. Perhaps they'll utter a fatalistic statement such as: 'I have an addictive personality.'

To which you can now answer, 'Perhaps, my dear. But more likely you have low self-efficacy.'

Once I started going to London for gigs, my capacity for embarrassing myself reached a grander scale, in front of an older, loftier audience that I would have killed for approval from. Alone on the train to Paddington, I drank a concoction of spirits decanted into a Timotei shampoo bottle, revelling in the sideways glances of other travellers (the flip side of embarrassment is defiance, after all). Upon arrival I'd buy a quarter-bottle of cheap vodka from the shop outside the station that didn't mind underage patrons. I'd slide that bottle into the curve of my back, secured by the waistband of my fishnets, so that I could smuggle it into the Garage, or Underworld, or Brixton Academy.

Inside the venue I'd hopefully find people I knew and, fuelled by shampoo, would shoot from first gear to fifth. Bands were great but, with my few coins already spent at the corner shop, my primary mission was theft of substances. No pack of cigarettes could be safely put down without me slipping it into my pocket. I'd steal a person's pint the moment they looked away or, failing that, would slurp spilt beer off tables, only partly for effect. I aimed for older men who, if they caught me in the act, would usually be appeased by a cheeky grin and a hasty flounce off in the opposite direction.

Without enough booze, I was cripplingly self-conscious. I'd fold in on myself as I stood watching a band, convinced every pair of eyes was assessing me critically (which, fair enough, they might be, if they'd met me before). The sense of scrutiny was intense. So I'd drink hard and fast to let myself off the leash, and then within the hour I'd be doing cartwheels across the room, stage-diving, stacking it, pouring a pint over someone's head or pulling a backbend by the bar, occasionally tipping over into something like a bloody punch-up in a cab queue or smashing up a phone box. It was a funny way of going about gaining that approval. Certainly, it had a shelf life.

Well into my twenties I'd lie awake at night in my room adorned with nightlife trinkets – tiki bar, ball gowns, vintage alcohol advertising – overcome with hot shame. My coping mechanism was to tell myself that everyone else was mundane. Their ideas were boring, their sex was suburban, their drinking, lightweight. I twisted the words of that Madness song into a new personal mantra: 'I am *beyond* embarrassment.' From shame to shameless. Sleep, when it came, brought with it recurring nightmares of plummeting lifts, crashing cars and planes, and tidal waves.

According to Dr Matthew Gullo, my behaviour is known as 'rash impulsivity'. Gullo is a clinical psychologist and senior research fellow at the Centre for Youth Substance Abuse Research, based out of the University of Queensland. There, he unravels the neuropsychological and cognitive mechanisms behind adolescent impulsivity. Kids who live by the motto 'everything harder than everyone else', kids for whom life is a desperate race to the bottom of the pile, they're his kind of kids.

Brisbane's precincts regularly erupt in late-night violence. Another clinician based in the city tells me about the ever-inventive ways local kids abuse drugs, from chewing Fentanyl patches, ordinarily used to alleviate terminal cancer pain, to brewing the toxic hallucinogenic flower Angel's Trumpet. These things rarely end well – in fact, they'll often end with death, or at least in the emergency ward – so what's the incentive?

Gullo tells me impulsivity is about fifty per cent genetic. The rest might be attributed to stressful upbringing, which affects the development of the brain regions involved in impulse control. Serotonin also plays a part through its regulation of behavioural control, but its role is still ambiguous.

'For a long time we thought impulsivity was this singular, straightforward thing, which is doing something in the moment without thinking through the consequences,' Gullo says, 'but there's a consensus emerging that it involves at least two key components.'

The first is known as reward drive, which is responsiveness to rewards and the motivational urge to obtain those rewards. It engages the reward pathway (technically known as the mesolimbic dopamine system) and the prefrontal regions of the brain connected to it. The reward drive could be compared to a car with a powerful engine: the slightest touch of the accelerator sends the revs into the red.

The second key component is rash impulsivity. 'It's that element of not taking into account future consequences,' explains Gullo, 'or, at least, those consequences aren't enough to stop you in the moment.' Back to the car metaphor: this model has problems with its brakes. It's like the way you conveniently forget how bad your last 'never again' hangover was.

Gullo and his research team developed the first human laboratory model of adolescent impulsivity and alcohol use. The lab was set up to investigate both whether the team could induce impulsivity in anyone, and whether the young subjects most enthusiastic about booze shared a certain gene. Essentially the researchers triggered impulsivity in their eighteen- to twenty-one-year-old subjects, then introduced a tray of booze.

There were three ways in which the team might trigger impulsivity. The first was to give people frustrating and complex mental tasks. This induces cognitive fatigue, which means they're less able to control their impulses. The second was to induce a negative emotional state by getting people to think about a vivid, upsetting memory for five minutes while they listen to some really depressing classical music. The third was via the reward-stimuli trigger: they were shown film clips that drove home the message that drinking is fun. Boys were shown a blast of *American Pie 2*. For girls, it was *Gossip Girl* (of which Gullo had to watch a whole season to find a suitable ten-minute clip).

Once an impulsive state was induced, the subjects were asked to do a 'taste rating test' on that selection of alcohol. 'Their job was to go through these drinks and rate them, but we were actually measuring how much they drank,' says Gullo. 'People who were higher on that reward-drive trait tended to drink more. We took some saliva and found that those who had the "at-risk" version of the gene RASGRF2, which has recently been identified in a European study, really responded to this induced impulsivity and drank more alcohol.'

Gullo says that, while males tend to be more reward-sensitive (more likely to notice and pursue rewards such as money, highs, acclaim and sex), men and women are fairly equal when it comes to inhibition control, which is the ability to put the brakes on. To put the conclusions into a fictional scenario, a teenage girl at high risk of impulsive drinking might be under stress (resulting in cognitive fatigue), surrounded by a family of drinkers (which gives those social-reward messages), and of a low-resilience temperament (known as negative affect).

The danger here is the adolescent brain can literally be shaped by substance use. At particular risk is the white matter, or nerve tissue, which is responsible for relaying information between cells. Neuroscientist Susan Tapert of the University of California has described 'little dings' in white matter when examining the brain scans of heavy-drinking twelve- to fourteen-year-olds. In girls, the effect of this damage tends to be poor performance in spatial functioning, which includes navigation, recognition of faces and scenes, and the observation of fine details. Boys tend to fare worse on focusing their attention.

Tapert also found that heavy use affects the hippocampus, which is a key area for memory formation and learning. Her young drinkers fared worse on tests of learning verbal material than the non-drinking control group. It also seems likely that having a drink as an adult can immediately worsen memory problems. Experiments with rats have found that subjects exposed to heavy alcohol use in adolescence performed worse on memory tasks as adults after a low dose of alcohol than the control groups. It's almost as if having a drink pulls a trigger.

When we think of impulsivity, we tend to think of the teenage boys who make the newspapers: for train surfing, joy-riding, tagging tall buildings, and getting all *Jackass* without the insurance policy. But perhaps impulsivity is just expressed differently in girls.

In every society, girls are expected to regulate their behaviour more readily than boys and to set a better example than their male classmates. 'They're so *imma-chewar*,' the girls in my class would observe of the boys as soon as we hit ten or so. As a rule, it's boys who tend to display 'externalising behaviour' – also known as 'acting-out disorders' – which includes aggression, oppositional behaviour, hyperactivity and attention problems. Girls are more commonly associated with 'internalising behaviour', such as anxiety, depression and social withdrawal. Punishment sensitivity also makes girls less inclined to engage in serious criminal behaviour.

Yet many studies have concluded that girls start experimenting with substances earlier than boys, and that females can outdo males in impulsivity in that area. Take the 2013 US study that surveyed kids in ten Connecticut high schools about high-risk behaviours and their use of cigarettes, cannabis and alcohol. The conclusions revealed that the boys had greater impulsivity, but that it wasn't connected to using substances; whereas, with the girls, impulsivity was directly connected to substances. Other studies have found that, among adolescents, female smokers appear more impulsive than male smokers; and among heavy drinkers, females exhibit poorer inhibitory control than males. High-five to the ladies.

The other overtly female path of impulsivity is reckless sex, which can be both a social tool for women, and a symptom of an underlying disorder that features impulsivity, such as bipolar or borderline personality. I go into that more fully in chapter seven.

Back to the showboating stunts and criminal behaviour of boys, though, and I do wonder if girls just get away with these things more because the gender stereotype is of easily influenced accomplice, rather than instigator. Boys end up in the criminal justice system, while girls – perhaps more willing to disclose their underlying problems – are more likely to wind up in the mental health system.

An informal Facebook poll was in order to see if the women I knew had any behaviour in their teenage pasts that could match up to the epic stupidity of teenage boys. Here are some of the responses I received from sensation-seeking sisters.

Friend 1: We jumped off ropes into waterholes. Drank goon around fires near the cliff-edges. Crossed train tracks to bush hideouts to smoke bongs. Packed eight people in a car to go search for magic mushrooms.

Friend 2: The fad with the cool girls in Year 7 was the 'passing out' game – basically depriving yourself of oxygen, so that when you came to you got a little head spin.

Friend 3: Spraying aerosol deodorant into a lid and drinking it for the alcohol.

Friend 4: We bonnet-bashed while drunk on West Coast Cooler – clinging to the bonnet of the car as it drove around a paddock.

Friend 5: We'd turn aerosol deodorant into blowtorches.

Friend 6: We'd pile into a Torana, drunk, and speed along the notoriously dark and windy roads of the park at the top end of town, with the headlights off.

To these I can add my own youthful adventures: Buying every legal high in Camden Market, then ticking off every illegal one: hash, acid, mushrooms, mescaline, ecstasy, speed, cocaine, ketamine, heroin, crack. Lighting fires in the bathroom. Practising the art of escape, daily, by jumping drunk out of my parents' second-storey bathroom window. Crashing the family car on a forty-five-second joy-ride. Getting into the car of drunken strangers, which caught fire when it swung off an embankment and into a tree. Insisting my (largely mute) mini-cab driver cut short his shift and join me in Soho's premier glam-metal club, Gossips. Getting frogmarched out of a venue for being sexy in the toilets. Falling down a staircase into a table of cocktails at a celebrity violinist's house and punching a fellow guest.

If you want to play along at home and gauge how impulsive you are, there are some personality tests available on the internet. I aced the Barratt Impulsiveness Scale, the Zuckerman Sensation-Seeking Scale, and Carver and White's Fun-Seeking Scale, so I can't blame youthful exuberance anymore.

Of most interest to me was Cloninger's Temperament and Character Inventory (TCI). Dr C. Robert Cloninger is a professor of genetics, psychiatry and psychology who developed the TCI as a personality test that can also be used as a diagnostic tool by professionals.

The TCI identifies four temperament traits (novelty seeking; harm avoidance; reward dependence; persistence) that describe our emotional drives and that often unconsciously determine our behaviour. They're about fifty per cent genetic and fifty per cent dependent on environment, culture and our choices. In addition, we have three character traits (self-directedness; cooperativeness; self-transcendence). These are ways we have intentionally shaped ourselves, based around goals, values and actions.

I connect by Skype with Julie, a counsellor from Cloninger's Wellbeing Coaching Program. She explains: 'On a good day our character traits are in charge, helping us govern our emotional drives. If we're sick or stressed, those character traits might be asleep and we'll be more ruled by our emotional drives.'

So what does a booze hound's inventory look like? I'd scored high average in the novelty-seeking temperament. Of its subtraits I scored highest on impulsivity. Yet I also scored a high average in the harm-avoidance temperament, specifically being sensitive to criticism and punishment. In all three tests now – Zuckerman, Carver and White, and Cloninger – I peaked in two conflicting areas: novelty seeking and avoidance.

It's a recognised mismatch, actually. In her book *Unbroken Brain: A Revolutionary New Way of Understanding Addiction* (2016), neuroscience journalist Maia Szalavitz describes three well-known routes into addiction that are supported by many longitudinal studies: the first being impulsivity; the second, anxiety and inhibition; and the third a mixture of these two opposing drives, in which an individual swings wildly from one to the other. Szalavitz says, 'My own story spirals around this paradoxical situation: I was driven enough to excel academically and fundamentally scared of change and of other people – yet I was also reckless enough to sell cocaine and shoot heroin.' She puts the paradox down to difficulty in self-regulation, a theme I explored in chapter one.

Julie tells me: 'Anecdotally I've heard drug and alcohol clinicians say that high harm avoidance is common among their clients because drugs help us adapt when we're feeling fearful.

But we can't satisfy two emotional drives at the same time. If you have two in conflict that doesn't feel good.' Right – much like the cognitive dissonance described in chapter two.

With another temperament trait, persistence, I scored high average. That sounds positive, but when applied to drugs and alcohol, not so much. 'Persistence can help you persevere to a goal, but it could be a goal of getting high or staying in an abusive relationship,' Julie says.

In terms of character traits, I scored a high average in self-directedness, particularly high in the sub-trait purposefulness. 'This means goals in alignment with values, and accepting responsibility for our own choices and mistakes,' according to Julie. 'People who are lower are always the victim of circumstance. They feel very unlucky.'

This was progress. While I was still drinking I would have scraped the lowest score, unless you count 'striving for the perfect level of drunk' as purposefulness, and now I was soaring. 'Lower self-directedness is common in people who are in very early recovery or not yet in recovery at all,' Julie tells me. 'There's so much research done with the TCI that is clear that the higher you are in self-directedness, the more it helps you if you have a mental health issue or if you are in recovery.'

There's no right or wrong score, of course. As Julie says, 'We all have these emotional drives and society needs all kinds. We need artists and musicians, just as we need bookkeepers and accountants.'

Dr Matthew Gullo says something similar. 'Impulsivity's not a bad thing. Natural selection would have weeded it out a long time ago if it was.' He points out that some of the most interesting and fun people in our lives are more impulsive than average. Impulsive risk-takers are more likely to get a leadership position and tend to make better venture capitalists. 'Think about Richard Branson,' he says. 'Who'd be silly enough to throw all this money into having a commercial space flight program going? Huge risks, and yet, if he pulls it off, millions and millions of dollars.'

I'm not one of those people with a copy of Richard Branson's *Losing My Virginity* in the lavatory but, like Rich, I've always enjoyed taking a gamble and liked to think that fortune favoured the brave, so all the more was the shock when my decision-making didn't work out. Then in my mid-thirties, I had a breakthrough. One problem I had always been able to identify but not solve was getting 'impulse' and 'instinct' muddled up. You're told to trust your instincts, but mine were forever urging: *Say that thing you ought not say. Proposition that person. Or, failing that, the other person. What happens if you try that? Do it.*

Finally, I figured out a foolproof distinction. Instinct is what tells us to run away from something; impulse is what tells us to run into it head on.

PART TWO

GENDERED ADVENTURES IN ADDICTION

4

TOTAL CONTROL

Self-destruction as a method of autonomy

When a person's behaviour is said to be 'out of control', the exact opposite may be true. They may be wresting control back.

My teens were a distilled version of the US's War on Drugs: all prohibition and punitive measures. My mother had made me sign a four-page contract without my lawyer present, packed with clauses that prohibited my favourite activities. A curfew was established that only allowed me to walk home from school at a brisk pace. Allowances were made for small privileges in exchange for lengthy chores. The lock on my door was removed, as was the red light bulb in my room; apparently it didn't look groovy and psychedelic – it made the house look like a brothel.

From this point on, alcohol became a form of psychic emancipation. I was fifteen and blind drunk every day after school. How was I managing it? Nobody knew. I was the David Copperfield of drinking. Every time the key was hidden to the drinks cabinet, I'd pride myself on finding it. In Dad's desk drawer? Laughable. Behind the salt cellar? Come on. After a while I got my own key cut at the cobbler's on Slough High Street so that I didn't need to bother playing the game. When I was finally rumbled and forced to hand that over, I resorted to Dad's terrible home-brew in the shed, which yeastily expanded the gut and sent one into quite the stupor. Tiring of that, I just broke into the cabinet with an icing spatula.

'It's like you *want* to get caught,' Mum would snap, amending the contract at the kitchen table.

It was true I was careless, but I didn't feel I was doing anything wrong. I wasn't out joy-riding, vandalising or doing anything that required an actual lawyer. Breaking into the drinks cabinet wasn't in order to party. It was more akin to a fox chewing off its own leg: escapism.

As the jaws clamped tighter around me, autonomy was achieved through more imaginative methods. Every time I felt enraged I got another hole punched in my ear. When I started getting frisked at the front door as I left, I'd buzz-cut another few inches of hair off my scalp when I got home. My body became our battlefield. On the occasions my behaviour was actually questioned, I'd flare up so defensively it would deter a seasoned hostage negotiator.

You are harming yourself, Mum wrote, in a letter I found upon waking one morning. It was time-stamped with my evening's adventures: *10.45pm: Telephone call from a police officer at Paddington Station*, through to *1.05am: You are carried off the train in comatose condition*. In retrospect, she was right. While getting wasted could certainly be joyous over the years – nights spent pelting through the streets of new cities, riding shopping trolleys into gutters, watching the sunrise from rooftops, having deep-and-meaningfuls in hazy corners – right then I was exploiting alcohol's capacity for expressing my independence. Badly.

These days, my mum is the glue that binds us all together, but during this particular period, with little support from any of us, our house rang to a Stravinsky symphony of banging doors. I'd retreat to my bedroom and put Hanoi Rocks's 'Dead by Christmas' on repeat. From its opening stabs of piano to the celestial fade out, it was forthright in its message. I knew Mum was monitoring my playlists because she'd recently come in to ban a Mötley Crüe ballad about the singer murdering his girlfriend.

My brother left home; now it was just the three of us. From a campus postbox he sent little life rafts. *Don't be too hard on Mum ... I know it's difficult ... Stick it out.* The letters came as a surprise, but they kept coming. Years later, I still get one of three voices in my head if I'm facing a fear. One's critical. One's anxious. The reasonable one, suggesting I take some kind of sensible option, is him.

I plotted my escape nonetheless: out of the house, out of Slough, and out of the country. I started speaking in an American accent. I went to Heathrow Airport on Saturdays and haunted the terminals. (Much later I learned Mum sometimes did, too.) At night I dreamed of train stations, timetables and maps. Maybe one day I'd shut the front door behind me and keep going past school, on and on, like Laurie Lee in *As I Walked Out One Midsummer Morning*.

When I reached sixteen, Mum conceded that I was better off drinking in company than alone and drove me to the pub every

Friday and Saturday night. This was employing the harm-minimisation approach favoured by Australia, rather than the hardline War on Drugs. Her liberalism went unrewarded when she'd have to use the DJ's PA system to find me, or be greeted by the police as I slumped on the pavement.

What else is a form of psychic emancipation? Well, there's a triumvirate of self-destructive behaviour. As well as problematic substance use (or you might swap in compulsive sexual behaviour), there are eating disorders and self-mutilation. The three can often rotate or coexist. Through their physicality they offer relief from inner, circular thoughts. Drinking feels like drowning oneself; taking drugs feels like obliteration. Self-mutilation takes the focus of pain from emotional to a precise point on the body. Throwing up is the literal purging of shame.

Eating disorders and self-mutilation, in particular, are very female coping mechanisms. As a generalisation, girls internalise their rage more readily than boys, exploring how much they hate themselves with an almost clinical curiosity. They're more likely to beat themselves up than bash somebody else. Any act of aggression against one's own body is also an act of regaining ownership of it, which can be particularly appealing to a woman with little autonomy.

At school, I noticed that my friend was whittling away into her arm with her set of compasses during maths class. I pulled up my sleeve and showed her my own homework. A couple of years later, Richey Edwards, the guitarist of indie band Manic Street

Preachers, would gash '4 REAL' into his arm with a razorblade during a major *NME* interview, requiring seventeen stitches. Suddenly, cutting yourself mangle-bangles was all out in the open.

The unimaginative comment about one who cuts is: 'They're just doing it for attention.' That may be true (and god forbid you give them some), but not everybody self-harms visibly. In fact, there's a worrying rise in anonymous self-trolling. The most notable case is that of UK teenager Hannah Smith, who killed herself in 2013. A police investigation revealed that the comments she'd received online – suggesting she cut herself and drink bleach – had likely been posted by herself. A self-cyberbullying study by the Massachusetts Aggression Reduction Center reveals that case was anything but a one-off.

But it's eating disorders that can have the most complex relationship with substance use, because of the way that different substances enable different forms of eating disorder. Research from Columbia University has found that three per cent of the general population have eating disorders. When we narrow that population down to people with problematic substance use, the figure rises to thirty-five per cent.

Anorexia nervosa tends to coexist with the use of stimulants – which suppress the appetite – rather than with alcohol (as well as its calorific content, alcohol makes it harder to lose weight because the body wants to burn off toxins before it turns its attention to fat and sugar). For many women who use stimulants, weight loss is a happy bonus. For others it's the primary motivation, known as circumstantial drug use. Cocaine alters the metabolism, reducing the body's ability to store fat. Smoking can provide the oral stimulus needed to trick the brain into being satisfied, as well as releasing the dopamine that would also be released by eating. Prescription drugs can promote weight loss, too. While doctors are less willing to prescribe addictive diet pills these days, speedy ADHD medication is increasingly prescribed to school-aged girls. Interestingly, not only are women with ADHD more likely to abuse substances, but they're at increased risk of developing eating disorders.

As a footnote to anorexia, it's ironic that orthorexia – which is the obsession with healthy, healing food – is also starting to be associated with stimulant use, anecdotally at least. This disorder is popular among Instagram's #cleaneating #fitspo #thinspiration advocates, but sometimes the desire to be thin rather than to be healthy is the underlying impetus.

Then there's binge-eating, which has well-established links with overconsumption of alcohol. In fact, multiple studies of patients who have undergone weight-loss surgical procedures found that the likelihood of these individuals abusing alcohol increases significantly once their hunger for food lessens. Some experts put this down to the individual suddenly having fewer enzymes with which to metabolise the alcohol, but there's a competing theory that someone who binge-eats could have a dopamine deficiency that will spur them to compulsively seek out other high-reward activities. It's certainly possible that one comforting behaviour might replace another, almost as if a person is eating or drinking their feelings. As journalist William Leith writes in his memoir *The Hungry Years: Confessions of a Food Addict*, 'Inside the binge, you are pure hunger – pure aspiration. Nothing else. You have created a time zone more present than the present.'

Disordered eating is often the accidental by-product of substance use. A boozy night is punctuated by a kebab, followed by a hungover day of eating carbs – all to be atoned for by a bout of starvation. In 2012 the *Mirror* in the UK reported on 'drunkorexia'. Women skip meals so they can go binge-drinking without putting on weight. Alcohol also gives them the feeling of being full. Then, of course, there's the matter of priorities – if you're on a bender, you don't really have time to eat. If you're on pills, you're certainly not hungry.

Finally, there's bulimia nervosa. Up to fifty per cent of people living with this eating disorder also experience problematic substance use, according to a combined study from Deakin University and Griffith University. Women with bulimia who also use substances have been shown to have higher dispositions toward impulsivity and novelty seeking.

The brother of Amy Winehouse has stated that it was bulimia that ultimately killed the singer, weakening her body so much that a bout of drinking gave her alcohol poisoning. Winehouse's previous heavy drug use – largely heroin and crack – absolutely wouldn't have helped, but the eating disorder had visibly ravaged her. Bulimia itself can cause sudden death due to cardiac or respiratory arrest from electrolyte imbalances due to constant purging. The depletion of vital minerals such as potassium, chloride and sodium can cause heart arrhythmia and kidney failure.

Eating disorders tend to flare up in times of stress or transition. When Winehouse was rising to fame with her debut album,

Frank, she was transitioning from a mouthy London girl with a love of weed to the giant talent who spawned a spate of poor imitations. Circa *Frank*, the same tabloids that later rubber-necked over her gauntness were applauding her for being curvy. Anyone can imagine the sort of backhanded compliments those appeared to her, designed to strike fear into the heart of the entire female demographic. *Relaxed singer celebrates her new curves. Star insists she's never felt happier in her own body* – that kind of thing.

Winehouse's bulimia started in her late teens (and, she told *Q* magazine, she started cutting herself at the age of nine) when – according to her brother Alex – her group of friends would 'put loads of rich sauces on their food, scarf it down and throw it up'. The learning of bulimia is usually vicarious in this way. Take the comedic scenes in teenage movies about high-school airheads – such as *Bring It On: All or Nothing; Wild Child; Sorority Row* and *Cruel Intentions* – in which girls trot off en masse to the toilets. In *Heathers*, one character demands of another, 'Where's your urge to purge?'

Just as there are 'Ana' websites dedicated to the sharing of anorexia tips, so there are 'Mia' sites for bulimia. On one, a pinned post offers harm-reduction tips. There are also plenty of threads about binging and purging while using substances. Some girls discuss the fact that they binge-eat when stoned and then need to redress the balance by purging once they sober up. Aside from weight loss, the reasons on this forum given for binging and purging include low self-esteem, anxiety, depression and admiration of one's own willpower – all things that could be applied to a person with problematic substance use.

That dichotomy was evident in Winehouse, who both picked apart her character flaws in her lyrics and made no effort to conceal her addictions. In the toilets of a high-end recording studio, it was reported in the documentary *Amy*, she redecorated a stall with vomit splatter and left it there. Perhaps it was pushback: Winehouse had no control left over her life, and her body became a very public act of defiance. She was hopelessly entwined with the needs of another person with problematic use: her husband. She was bundled off planes and onto stages by her management. She was hemmed in at home by the paparazzi. There was no period factored in for recovery. By the time she refused to sing at the fated Belgrade concert and instead took a seat on the stage, she was practically a prisoner of her schedule.

In many ways, her situation isn't unusual. Ordinary girls are hounded by their own self-inflicted paparazzi: Instagram, Snapchat, other social media. They're compelled, pressured and shamed into capturing themselves as a commodity in every waking hour. In this sense, an eating disorder can be reframed by the individual as a valid tool, rather than a problem. Winehouse might have viewed her bulimia as a useful technique for a celebrity in the public eye. Certainly it's not uncommon for athletes, gymnasts and ballerinas to purge as part of their body maintenance. Mixed martial arts star Ronda Rousey has admitted to substance abuse and bulimia while training as a young woman.

It doesn't take much imagination to visualise the desire for success – be it work goals, sporting achievements, or platinum records – malfunctioning, so that punishing the body becomes its own magnificent feat of endurance.

To understand the links between eating disorders and problematic substance use, I speak to Natalie Loxton, senior lecturer in psychology at Griffith University and an honorary senior research fellow at the University of Queensland's Centre of Youth Substance Abuse Research. For her, much of the commonality between the two boils down to sensitivity of the reward system. This system is central to humans evolving, so it's responsive to sex and falling in love, but also rewarding activity such as drug-taking and the consumption of high-sugar, high-fat food.

Reward sensitivity is considered to be a personality trait, an innate difference that we all have. People who are reward-sensitive have a lower density of dopamine-releasing neurons and so seek out more stimulation, such as from drugs. The problem is, research indicates that they have an inefficient system for maintaining homeostasis, or balance. This means not only will they feel the urge to seek out more stimulation, but once they have it they'll release more dopamine than the average person. They'll find this rewarding and aim to repeat the experience.

'If you think of small children, some are hypersensitive to anything that's stimulating in the environment, and others are less so,' says Loxton. 'That's the trait that we've been looking at. Who's more likely to expand that into drugs and alcohol when they're adolescent?'

In 2012, researchers at Columbia University used PET scans to monitor the brains of fifteen women with bulimia and fifteen without, and concluded that the women with bulimia had reduced dopamine release, something that has also been observed in people with substance dependence.

In one of Loxton's own studies, in which Year 11 and 12 girls in Brisbane self-reported through questionnaires, her team found that heightened sensitivity to reward was a better predictor of alcohol misuse, while dysfunctional eating usually relied upon two things: heightened sensitivity to reward and heightened sensitivity to punishment. Perhaps we might deduce from this that someone who is a big drinker might also develop an eating disorder if they have underlying anxiety. Food obsession pushes out intrusive thoughts.

So there's a strong case for a biological predisposition to substance abuse and eating disorders but, as Loxton reminds us: 'Nothing exists in a vacuum.' There are the socialisation and sociocultural factors, too.

Family's a key one. Binging – on food, drugs, or alcohol – is often trans-generational, in that it can be influenced by parental over-indulgence or dieting behaviours. Family dysfunction and trauma can also lead to a lack of the behavioural skills required to process difficult emotions.

Then there's our style of attachment to our parents. It's through our attachment that we form an internal working model of the value of ourselves and the dependability of others. There are four attachment styles as outlined by child-development psychologist John Bowlby, only one of which – secure attachment – is healthy. If an individual has experienced one of the three types of insecure attachment – ambivalent-anxious (such as an inconsistent parent, veering between nurturing, neglectful and intrusive); avoidant-anxious (such as a parent who is cold and unavailable); and disorganised/disoriented (such as an erratic or abusive parent) – their emotional development may suffer and the individual may turn to food or substances for comfort.

Both eating disorders and problematic substance use can be life-threatening and require intensive therapy, despite which there will be high relapse rates. The shared risk factors include low self-esteem, depression, anxiety, or impulsivity; unhealthy parental behaviours; and peer and social pressures. There's also sometimes a history of sexual or physical abuse that, as I've said, can spur a need to regain control over the body, but which can also prompt a desire to disappear from view: *If I starve myself, nobody will notice me. If I overeat, no one will want to touch me and I'll become invisible.*

The biggest challenge about having a coexisting – also known as 'comorbid' – eating disorder and substance use problem comes when seeking treatment. Firstly, because people with eating disorders often conceal the fact or are fearful of putting on weight; and secondly, because finding a facility that will treat both issues once they've become severe is extremely difficult in Australia.

To tackle the first issue: a woman who is using stimulants and finds that – either by accident or design – the drugs enable weight loss, might be fearful of stopping use. On the harm-minimisation website *Bluelight*, one user describes her ambivalence about quitting meth. 'The second time I tried to quit and went up almost two dress sizes, it really freaked me out,' she writes. 'As petty an issue as it may seem to some, this is a serious issue, which really contributes to my hesitation in stopping, despite how bad meth is.'

Some drug and alcohol workers whom I've spoken to for this book describe 'rehab spread' – the combined effect of quitting drugs and suddenly getting three square meals a day. Glenda Milne from Guthrie House in Sydney tells me her staff has to monitor behaviour at mealtimes. 'They won't eat,' she says of the residents. 'Drugs have given them this svelte figure and they like that. Of course, when they come off drugs their appetite returns and they start to put all the weight on, then it creates another set of behaviours that says, "Well, I'm not going to eat, I'm going to take laxatives." They weren't necessarily anorexic before, but they're now conscious of the fact that they've put on weight and they don't like it.'

So yet another commonality that eating disorders have with problematic substance use is self-concealment. Very often, the individual is honest neither to themselves nor to treatment providers about the extent of what's going on. In one 2008 study, respondents with eating disorders reported a variety of strategies used to conceal their habits to others. They also didn't recognise the health risks listed in the survey as applying to themselves, and will downplay to themselves the frequency of their behaviour. In *Eating Disorders Review*, Walter Vandereycken summarised: 'research on denial has been hampered by a lack of agreement as to whether it is unconscious or conscious, a trait versus a state, an indication of psychological disturbance, or a functional coping mechanism.'

In her memoir *How to Disappear Completely: On Modern Anorexia*, journalist Kelsey Osgood writes, 'It never occurred to me to try to lose weight in any healthy way, or to strive for a body that "looked good". I wanted to be repulsively thin.' Osgood describes hospital wards where there's always a resident 'best' anorexic, just as I've been in AA meetings where people have joked about being the 'best little alcoholic'. Whereas I prided myself on repeatedly cracking the code of the drinks cabinet, girls living with anorexia learn tricks, such as rubbing soup into wooden tables, that make monitoring their eating very difficult for staff. There's that secret thrill of getting one over somebody; the satisfaction of being smarter.

On to the second issue, of not being able to find treatment: women who develop severe cases of substance dependence and anorexia that require acute medical care can find themselves in a deadly catch-22. Unless they manage to find a hospital-based service or specialised private care, somebody who is intoxicated is unlikely to be admitted to an eating-disorder ward, because it won't have the necessary medications or trained staff to deal with withdrawal. The flip side is that somebody with a dangerously low body mass index won't be admitted to many detoxes or rehabs, as the facility won't have the medical set-up, nor the insurance, to treat a severe eating disorder.

This leaves two probable outcomes. The first is that the individual lies about the severity of their drug use and seeks treatment at an eating-disorder clinic, riding out any withdrawal on their own. Upon release they often go back again and use, because their substance use has not been tackled. The second is that an individual with a less-visible eating disorder chooses to tackle their substance use first. But bouncing between two services in such a way means that, at best, an individual's suffering is prolonged and, at worst, the extended process could cost them their life.

What's the answer? Ideally, catching an eating disorder before it becomes too severe for some drug and alcohol facilities to treat. Eating disorders could be screened for when a new client accesses a drug and alcohol service, or visits their GP – particularly because the physical manifestation of a disorder such as bulimia isn't always obvious. Tools are available, such as the Eating Disorder Examination Questionnaire (EDEQ) and SCOFF (Do you make yourself Sick because you feel uncomfortably full? Do you worry you have lost Control over how much you eat? Have you lost more than One stone in a three-month period? Do you believe yourself to be Fat when others say you are thin? Would you say that Food dominates your life?). According to the National Centre on Addiction and Substance Abuse report, it's particularly important to screen clients who are high caffeine users, smokers, girls at puberty, athletes, or those who use pharmaceutical drugs to reduce water retention, bloating, or induce purging.

Donna Ribton-Turner is the director of clinical services at drug treatment and education agency ReGen in Melbourne. She tells me that her counsellors see many people with undiagnosed eating disorders, so conversation about nutrition is vital. 'Our experience is that this is something that people only disclose once they have been engaged with a service for a while and have developed sufficient trust in the service,' says Ribton-Turner. 'It would be more effective to train counsellors and other AOD [alcohol and other drugs] workers in identifying and responding to eating disorders within the scope of their engagement, once a therapeutic relationship has been established.'

For those women whose eating disorder is not so severe that it prevents them from being admitted to a detox or rehab, there are some forms of treatment, such as cognitive behavioural therapy, ACT mindfulness and dialectical behaviour therapy, that are appropriate to use with both issues. These approaches can reinforce healthy thinking and tackle the shared characteristics of eating disorders and problematic substance use, which include obsessive preoccupation and compulsive behaviour; mood-altering effects; social isolation and secrecy. Additionally, the client would be taught about nutrition, exercise and sleep.

But there are also differences between the two issues, most significantly that eating disorders cannot be treated with abstinence. Instead, the habits themselves – starvation, binging, purging, body loathing and negative thoughts – must be replaced by positive behaviours. This means treatment services that offer a twelve-step approach are not ideal for the individual with a comorbid problem. As Adrienne Ressler of the Renfrew Centre eating-disorder clinics in the United States has noted in *Social Work Today*, during twelve-step recovery a client is taught that addiction is a disease and that the disease is their identity. For example, in a meeting they will introduce themselves with: 'My name is _____ and I am an addict.'

Yet it's not healthy for an individual to associate themselves with an eating disorder in this way. Very likely they will have been berating themselves with self-loathing mantras that have hijacked their self-image, so it's vital that they learn to separate their identity from the illness. It's additionally important that the individual with an eating disorder feels empowered after years of suffering low self-esteem, which is at odds to the twelve-step method of handing over control to a Higher Power.

As I'll go on to discuss in chapter fifteen, women's mental health issues can be so complex – often spanning trauma, drug use and an eating disorder – that holistic care is desperately needed, either within one facility, or by having facilities better connected to one another. And beyond this immediate, emergency care, there need to be services that offer ongoing support.

On that front, could Amy Winehouse, posthumously, have the answer? Over in London, Amy's Place has been founded in her name. It's funded by the Amy Winehouse Foundation and operated by a housing group, Centra. Women under thirty can stay for up to two years, to learn long-term coping skills. Some have been homeless; others have come from jail; and still others self-referred. The majority, as with Winehouse, have comorbid eating disorders and substance-use issues.

With all this in mind, do you want to take a punt on what my newfound hobby was when I quit drinking? Not mindfulness. Not exercise. I started sticking my fingers down my throat. I just didn't realise it at the time.

How do you not notice being on your knees in the bathroom? Good question. I think you just compress the number of occasions to one or two, like taking a photo in burst-mode. I did sometimes acknowledge to myself that I was throwing up when uncomfortably full or if I'd eaten something that didn't agree with me (everything), but it wasn't until I'd gone down two dress sizes in two months and was constantly deflecting comments of concern that I had to face that gripping the toilet seat was a twice-daily occurrence. At that point I stopped immediately, which I was pretty pleased about. Until I noticed I was popping codeine every day.

It took moving office to notice *that*. This is self-concealment in action. I opened a desk drawer to clear it out and found six half-empty packets of cold-and-flu tablets that I couldn't recall buying. There were more in my bag and more at home, as it turned out, innocently stashed in the first-aid box. I did remember buying the first pack. I had a music festival coming up, at which I'd have to socialise for eight hours without the prop of booze or drugs. Taking these tablets, with their combo of codeine and buzzy pseudoephedrine, would be a form of harm-minimisation, I reasoned, in that they would minimise my need to nervously chain smoke.

Since then, I could picture the odd visit to a chemist, but not this many. I guessed that I had been packing my bag for work every morning and leaving the tablets behind – since, of course, I didn't need them – only to swerve into a chemist halfway through the morning when grabbing the third coffee of the day. Perhaps I told myself I needed tampons, or vitamins, or something. The codeine had been causing me to scratch my skin until it bled. My energy levels had plummeted, and I found it hard to engage my brain. I put all that down to some new food intolerance and cut out gluten.

It's funny how denial works, but not really surprising that when you take away one coping mechanism you seek another. Now I stay alert ... and occasionally alarmed.

5

AMATEUR ALCHEMY

Self-medicating mental illness and tweaking the personality

In 1996, *Trainspotting* was released. The opening 'choose life' monologue from its heroin-using protagonist, Rent Boy, is a scathing takedown of homogeneous society that an entire generation could soon repeat word for word.

Later in the film, Rent Boy observes: 'The streets are awash with drugs you can have for unhappiness and pain, and we took them all. Fuck it, we would have injected vitamin C, if only they'd made it illegal.'

That's not an ethos local to Edinburgh. In the initial pursuit of partying, people are likely to find themselves drawn to certain families of substances, and they will discover that these additionally offer relief to symptoms of mental illness, distress, or emotional pain. It's known as self-medication and it's a key reason that many people use drugs. In fact, a report from New South Wales, *Living Well NSW 2014*, found that three-quarters of people using mental health services also have substance-use issues.

The year *Trainspotting* came out I was twenty-one and had scored my first job, working at a music PR company in Soho. I self-medicated my phobia of talking on telephones by taking lots of amphetamine sulphate. Speed was wonderful. It dilated my pupils and opened my veins, and let the milk of human kindness flow through me. I felt calm, benevolent and expansive. And romantic and tragic and relevant.

'I can tell when you're on speed,' my boss said, having taken me aside into the schmooze-room in which we wooed bands and managers. 'You're a lot friendlier than usual.'

Something flickered in my peripheral vision. I whipped my head, but as usual I was too slow. These hallucinatory trails were following me more and more these days. I turned back to Adam. A few years earlier he'd found the *Slapper* debacle of chapter two very amusing, and offered to be the gatekeeper between me and the press, for free. I'd become the company mascot, then wound up interning there. And then Adam gave me my first job, which was quite surprising when you consider that during my internship I'd left a can of cider outside the door in the stairwell every day, to resume drinking it at lunchtime.

Adam had never mentioned the drinking. He was terribly English. Like now, for instance. If I was the sort of girl who was a bit dim, I might misinterpret his 'friendlier on speed' comment as his blessing, since he was loath to push it further. I mean, I was a PR, for godsake. I was supposed to be friendly, and emptying the best part of a gram of speed into my morning coffee was the only way it was going to happen. By day, the moist, yellowing powder sat fatly in its baggy inside my purse, waiting to give me a little dry-retch at the smell of it. I'd purse the lips of the bag and shake some more into my pint at lunchtime to tide me over, watching fascinated as it dissolved into the bubbles of my Strongbow.

Adam continued, 'I want us to be like Batman and Robin. A team.'

I let my eyes come to rest on the shoulder of his vintage bowling shirt. I felt a twinge of sympathy for Adam. My role was a junior one, but it was a really good opportunity for a new university graduate: call *NME* journalists to ask what they think of a record. Write press releases. Go to gigs. Escort musicians with poor life skills to and from the airport. But I was erratically moody. I genuinely felt that my problems were worse than anyone else's, and that this should earn me special dispensation.

I smiled magnanimously. He'd caught me on a good day, which was every other day. I'd give myself a day off speed after taking it, because it had a tendency to keep me up till four in the morning, writing a terrible novel at the kitchen table. It was hard to go to bed, because – as any woman who has cut her own fringe and wound up with it getting shorter and shorter will understand – I would finish what was intended to be my last cigarette, but still have a few gulps of fortified wine left in the glass. So to even things out I'd light another, but then would finish the wine halfway through it and so would have to top up the glass. It could take hours to get those two substances to conclude in sync. Anyway, I was never going to finish this book because I kept having real-life dramas that the protagonist then had to work through, destroying any chance of a narrative arc.

Here's a drama; a little vignette. Once, Adam found me sitting, dazed, outside a venue that one of our bands was playing. I confessed I'd been smoking crack – an interesting upgrade from speed – although it was outside of working hours, to be fair. 'That's not a very good idea, is it?' he said smoothly, and went in. Another time, after a pay-review meeting, I pummelled the toilet wall in a rage, until the tiles avalanched to the floor. I scooped them into my bag and went home. Later I found out my colleagues were briefed about the incident, but still nobody took me aside.

The final straw was the internet. It was fairly newfangled, and word had got around, via the CEO's personal assistant, that any email we deleted was being rerouted to the big man's inbox. A bunch of us junior employees leaned into the table at the local pub, disbelieving of this sorcery. Alison wanted me to know in particular, because my occasional special offers of five-quid bags of speed might be intercepted and get her into trouble. To test her theory, I went back to the office and sent the boss an email, via myself. I deleted it.

An hour later, I was called into the schmooze-room and fired. No specific reason was given. I was outraged. And then I was kicked out of my flat by my friend William, just two days after I moved in. I was outraged again, but we're still friends. He tells people I poured Strongbow Super on my cornflakes, whereas in fact I had used milk. In his mind he may have superimposed the can of Strongbow Super *next* to the bowl, *into* the bowl. That's okay. I can't claim to be the most reliable witness myself.

In both of these incidents, I considered Adam and William to be at fault. They knew I was troubled before they decided to lift me up, put me on a salary/their rental contract, then drop me again. I expected from them both a duty of care and more sense.

Anyway, I'd get a better job.

Women self-medicate more than men. It's a refrain that I hear over and over as I'm researching this book. According to a survey of 43,000 Americans by the National Institute of Alcohol Abuse and Alcoholism, women have stronger associations than men between problematic substance use and obsessive-compulsive, histrionic, schizoid, and antisocial personality disorders, while men have a stronger association between problematic substance use and dependent personality disorder. In general, women are considered to be more likely to use drugs and alcohol for reasons of negative reinforcement, such as to alleviate anxiety and depression, while men's reasons tend more towards positive reinforcement, such as getting wasted with the boys, or for performance enhancement.

But is that accurate? Or is the idea of self-medication itself prescriptive? Here's a new slant: Maybe women are widely believed to use substances to self-medicate because that's the sad little box we're supposed to stay in. God forbid we take drugs to enjoy ourselves.

I started considering this angle after interviewing Dr Nadine Ezard, the clinical director of the Alcohol and Drug Service at St Vincent's Hospital in Sydney. She tells me that Edward Khantzian, Professor of Psychiatry at Harvard Medical School, came up with the hypothesis of self-medication in the 1970s, and it's rarely challenged.

'You can be mad, sad, or bad ... but for women it's better to seem mad or sad,' she says. 'That morality still persists that young women aren't supposed to have fun or have a sexuality. It's problematic to me on every level. It's about this whole moral overtone: first of all, that medication should only come from someone else, preferably a male doctor; then the idea that self-medicating is less stigmatising than wanting to just get off your face. If you're maintaining an expensive coke habit, you're actually pretty functional and resilient, and those qualities need to be celebrated as well, in the stories that we make about ourselves.'

Maybe we women are even conditioned to view our own drug-taking as 'self-medication'; long-suffering pack mules that we are. Take the example of wine-o-clock memes, which often depict a Victorian-era woman, or a mother on the verge of a nervous breakdown. At wine-o-clock they're allowed to alleviate some stress, not simply enjoy a good-quality drop. As Professor Steve Allsop, director of the National Drug Research Institute, tells me, 'In the 1980s when I was working at an alcohol treatment centre in Scotland, if women came in it was assumed they were depressed. And they might have been, but no more than the men. It was just assumed there must be something wrong with them, rather than they had just been drinking too much and having a great time.'

Pathologising women is big business. We're significantly more likely to be prescribed psychotropic medication, and we outnumber men in diagnostic categories such as depression, anxiety and borderline personality disorder. The self-medicating housewife has been a tragic and pathetic figure in popular culture.

She's Marianne Faithfull's pathetic, pill-gobbling tragedy in 'The Ballad of Lucy Jordan'; perpetually smoking, forever unfulfilled Betty Draper in *Mad Men*; mean-drunk Martha in *Who's Afraid of Virginia Woolf*; and Kirsten, in *Days of Wine and Roses*, who accidentally sets fire to her apartment and almost kills her child. Just as 'hysteria' was the catch-all condition for frustrated women in Freud's day, 'anxiety' was the buzzword from the mid-twentieth century onwards. The best prescription would really have been a more fulfilling, less restrictive life.

That's certainly the view of Jane Ussher, who is a professor of Women's Health Psychology at the Centre for Health Research at Western Sydney University. She's written three books dissecting the idea of women's mental illness being both a reaction to misogyny and a misogynistic construct. *The Madness of Women: Myth and Experience* opens with the experiences of her own mother, who was treated for postnatal depression with a drug for schizophrenia, hospitalised and given electric shock therapy.

'She had four young children and a husband who was down the pub every night offering no support. She didn't have friends because my dad wouldn't let her, and she didn't work. I mean, who wouldn't be depressed,' Ussher says. 'One of the arguments is that women are treated biomedically through the body for distress that is a reaction to life situations. In fact, the real problem could be a relationship, or over-responsibility for the family, or lack of power.'

GPs aren't alone in pushing products at women. In decades past, big pharma marketers have actively encouraged women to self-medicate with over-the-counter goodies, such as with the addictive painkiller-and-caffeine combo Bex and its 1950s slogan: 'Stressful day? What you need is a cup of tea, a Bex and a good lie down.' This tranquillisation of women experiences waves of popularity, just as fashion does. In the 1960s it was Valium, immortalised in the Rolling Stones' hit 'Mother's Little Helper' (not to be confused with gin – mother's ruin), and Seconal, described as 'dolls' in Jacqueline Susann's *Valley of the Dolls*, and linked to the deaths of Judy Garland, Dina Washington and actor Lupe Vélez. In the 1970s it was Quaaludes, beloved by Sunset Strip groupies, who no doubt nicked them off their mums. In the 1980s it was Xanax. You get the idea.

Once dependent on these, the savvy individual will start 'doctor shopping' – visiting a range of psychiatrists, hospitals and GPs for prescriptions and relying on a lack of communication between services to benefit from multiple scripts. A study of 121 chronic pain patients published in *The Clinical Journal of Pain* in 2009 also found that women are more likely to hoard unused medications, in order to take larger doses, and to combine them with other drugs. Over-the-counter drugs, such as those containing codeine, can be just as dangerous.

It's when she needs to play amateur alchemist with her self-medication that a woman can really get into trouble. Let's say she can't sleep from the cocaine she's using to overcome her social anxiety. She goes to her GP, perhaps leaving out the coke bit, since it's not routinely asked about, and requests some barbiturates for insomnia. She might then help the barbs along with a bit of vodka, not realising that the combination of these two depressants could shut down her central nervous system. Reality TV star Anna Nicole Smith died when she combined a sedative with four types of benzos. Whitney Houston's toxicology report detailed cocaine, while also referencing the 'plethora' of twelve medicine bottles in the room, including anti-anxiety drug Xanax and muscle relaxer Flexeril, from five different doctors.

There are lots more examples of bad combinations that I certainly didn't know about before researching this book. Nicotine, used as stress relief, can react poorly with an anti-psychotic medication. Alcohol, used to soothe distress, can react with antidepressants to make someone behave more erratically. Ecstasy and antidepressants together can lead to dangerous, even fatal levels of serotonin, known as serotonin syndrome. Given that most pharmaceutical drugs are only tested on men anyway (as I'll explain in chapter fifteen), the outcomes on women are a particularly unknown quantity.

While I waited for my better job to arrive, a cleaning agency sent me to rarefied Belgravia and Chelsea, to the apartments of double-barrelled debutantes. These young women often lived in pairs, as I'd discover when they first distractedly took me on a tour of their surfaces. If they were nervous about handing the keys over to someone with skittish eyes and a uniform of Hawaiian shirt, ripped stockings and baseball boots, they hid it well.

It's funny. People go on about how speed makes you better at cleaning but, as an ex-cleaner myself, I can vouch that isn't a golden rule. As the iron ticked into life on the ironing board, I'd switch on the telly, pour a bowl of pistachios, and relieve the crystal decanter of some of its contents. Sometimes I'd nose in their drawers, as was my duty as an artiste. I fancied myself as Sophie Calle, who took a job as a chambermaid in a Venetian hotel and photographed the contents of suitcases and bathrooms, as though the room were a crime scene. She would read diaries, spray herself with cologne, rifle through clothes, try on makeup. Sometimes she'd stalk the guests, too, recording their conversations. *L'Hôtel, Chambre 47*, she called the collection.

I wasn't that bad and, as long as there was always someone worse, I was cool. The speed was really helping with my creativity, just as it had helped Philip K. Dick, Jack Kerouac, Graham Greene, Ayn Rand, and Jean-Paul Sartre before me. Without it, I couldn't focus my thoughts, which either pinballed around my head or popped like bubbles. With it – my god! The thunderous brilliance of my prose.

Since I was taking speed orally, my stomach was constantly grouching and clenching. For that, I bought Pepto-Bismol, which an American drummer had introduced me to, along with smack, which I didn't take to. In theory, it would dispel your nausea, but I swigged the pink stuff so regularly that it made my sickness worse. I got in the habit of sticking two fingers down my throat over the toilet to expedite the process.

One day one of the debutantes came home unexpectedly. I was in the kitchen, wiping down a surface with one hand and holding a Scotch in the other. Thank god I'd had the foresight to decant it into a mug. As Philippa (Pippa? Pip? Flip?) put down her keys and rummaged in a drawer for whatever it was she'd forgotten, the scent of whisky unfurled like a will-o'-the-wisp between us. I cradled my hands around the mug and blew on it, as if to cool down its contents. Philippa's eyes were wary, but she said nothing and left.

I'd got away with it. Speed makes you a bit arrogant like that, which was a good feeling in itself. There was a whole other world going on that these squares knew nothing about, and it was pinging around in my reward pathways.

Self-medicating usually occurs through trial and error ... in fact, many people wouldn't even consider that they were doing it. The biggest clue is that they're taking the drug when they're alone, outside the parameters of fun or experimentation.

For self-soothing anxiety there are the sedatives: heroin, benzodiazepines such as diazepam, alcohol, codeine, opioid prescription drugs and cannabis. Others are chosen for a shot of boldness, such as stimulants and that multi-tasker, alcohol. Those with depression might select a substance that offers a dramatic dopamine spike, such as methamphetamine. People living with bipolar disorder often juggle uppers and downers as they move through states and cycles, to try to maintain some semblance of normality. It's a haphazard way of going about things – stimulants, in particular, can trigger mania and psychotic symptoms – and, when prescribed medication is also in the equation, it can be disastrous.

Among adults, obsessive-compulsive disorder (OCD) affects more women than men. Often hereditary and exacerbated by stress, it's characterised by intrusive fears, such as of hurting oneself or others, or sexual fantasies, or obsessive thoughts about other people, and, often, poor impulse control. One 2009 study, published in the *Journal of Anxiety Disorder*, reported that more than twenty-five per cent of a sample of people seeking treatment for OCD met the criteria for a substance-use disorder. A 2010 report in *Molecular Psychiatry* reported thirty-eight per cent. OCD is associated with low levels of serotonin, which is why serotonin-boosting substances such as ecstasy and LSD hold great appeal.

People with undiagnosed attention deficit hyperactivity disorder (ADHD) will often opt for stimulants such as speed in an effort to calm a jumpy mind – quite the opposite to the way it affects others. There's also a lot of evidence that people with ADHD quite like drugs in general, though – perhaps, as ADHD specialist Dr Ellen Littman believes, because they're more likely to experience anxiety and depression, self-loathing, low self-esteem, self-harm and suicide attempts. A 2012 Dutch study found that ADHD was present in almost one in four people with a substance-abuse disorder that they screened.

When we think of ADHD we're transported back to the disruptive boy in the classroom, but it affects girls, too; it's just they tend to display the more attention-deficit symptoms, which is tougher to diagnose. Girls are easily dismissed as hair-twirling daydreamers, particularly in the 1980s when I was growing up, when – let's face it – not much was expected of girls at all.

The tide is turning. Between 2008 and 2012, the number of American women on ADHD medication rose by eighty-five per cent. This can in part be attributed to the fact that women who slipped through the cracks as children (on account of not being boys) are now getting a late diagnosis, on average between the ages of thirty-six and thirty-eight. Often the penny will drop for them when they take their sons to be diagnosed, because it's often hereditary.

Journalist Gina Pera, author of *Is It You, Me, or Adult ADD*?, tells me, 'As they grow older, girls might try to mask their disorganisation by adopting a non-conformist persona – smoking cigarettes, drinking alcohol, and having sex earlier than their peers.' It's not uncommon for her to hear from women who self-medicated with cocaine and methamphetamine. 'They report that it gave them a "clear head" for the first time in their life,' she says. 'And confidence. After a lifetime of feeling tentative and likely to screw up at any moment, confidence can be a welcome feeling.'

After two years of mopping floors, I finally landed myself a role fit for an unheralded genius, at a publishing company that put out noirish crime novels and cultish reissues. It was just me and the publisher, who offered to compensate my meagre salary by publishing my first novel – if I could just finish it.

The shake, shake, shake of a baggie into my drink had become incessant, and I had grown careless with my rule of sticking to the first half of the day. I was starting to suffer sleep paralysis, believing myself to be awake, with my eyes open, but gradually realising the flatmates I could hear talking weren't in the house. When I panicked I'd find myself frozen rigid.

The auditory hallucinations continued when I was wide awake. One afternoon I roamed the house searching for the radio that had been left on. I could hear the one-finger synth line of White Town's 'Your Woman' as clear as day, looping over and over, and it was getting on my wick. Eventually I traced it to the devil's wireless in my skull. Similarly, at night I might hear the crackle of a male voice through a walkie-talkie as I tried to fall asleep, or a fly buzzing on my eardrum. The only witness was my hamster, going around and around on its wheel.

I can pinpoint the moment speed really turned on me. At a pub with a friend, I'd complained about my appearance: that my legs were covered in sores that wouldn't heal and my face was constantly burning up. 'You're dehydrated, Jenny,' she said flatly. 'Speed dehydrates you.'

Back at home that night, her words rang in my ears like White Town. I headed for the kitchen tap and knocked back pint after pint. This was the same year as a billboard campaign warning of the dangers of ecstasy. The family of teenager Leah Betts wanted the last photo of her, hooked up to life support, to hit home with young people, much as the family of Anna Wood had a similar campaign, around the same time, in Australia. It was the subject of much snark from the warehouse ravers I hung out with, who liked to point out that Leah had died from drinking too much water in one go, not from ecstasy itself. Nevertheless, I remembered her photo a few pints into my rehydration tactic, and freaked out.

My brain was swelling like Leah's, I knew it. I collapsed in the hallway, all the sensation in my body disintegrating into a million tiny pieces. I dragged myself over to my flatmate's room and banged on the door, but she was either not in or not answering. (A year later she would sing 'ding dong, the witch is dead' when I moved out.)

I rang the dealer I sometimes slept with and told him I'd overdosed on speed. 'You can't overdose on speed,' he said and laughed, and I heard a girl laugh, too.

From that night on, speed made me sick every time I took it. I considered it an awful betrayal. I'd lost my writing mojo to the distractions of these new side effects. I'd lose sensation in my legs, my face and head, and would rake my fingers over my skin, desperate to feel something.

I enrolled in a drug and alcohol course in north London, to try to shed light on it all. The students would compare notes during smoke breaks about things they'd tried. One bloke recommended the best brand of glue to sniff. That was handy. I'd tried glue and only managed to stick the paper bag together. Craft projects aside, I spent weeks browsing the library at the now-defunct Institute for the Study of Drug Dependence in Holborn. Through extensive reading I identified amphetamine psychosis as a likely suspect for my mystery illness, but found nothing about numbness of the face and limbs. I began to suspect multiple sclerosis or diabetes.

I went to the doctor, and he prescribed Prozac.

But everyone's mentally ill in their twenties, aren't they? Everyone's drinking on antidepressants, smoking menthols, and listening to Nick Cave or his descendants. Of my housemates alone there was Connie, self-medicating what she believed to be bipolar disorder. She'd been hospitalised countless times for drunken suicide attempts, having had the sort of traumatic childhood I could only imagine. She'd asked me to move in to help look after her, though I could hardly look after myself.

Then there was Sofie, a sleepy-eyed Dane, who would vet future housemates with me by interviewing them over a foul bottle of port. If they drank it, they were in. Last I saw her, she'd accidentally set a share house on fire and barely escaped with only burned hands, having crawled to freedom.

Not long after that she was committed to a psychiatric ward after starting a fight with a policeman in a pub somewhere in Wales.

I have no idea where Sofie is now. I wish I could have been of some help to her, instead of no help at all. I believe I thought to myself at the time: *I've got my own problems.* Subtext: *And they're worse than yours.*

While researching this chapter, I was struck by a suspicion. I booked in to see my GP, to enquire about ADHD. I wasn't just going on my attraction to speed. If I apply the ADHD symptoms of hyperactivity, inattentiveness, impulsivity, poor working memory, and low-frustration tolerance to my life so far, the evidence stacks up.

Queue rage.
Flooding bathrooms.
Knee-jerk email rants.
Not following movie plots.
Cycles of short-term fixations.

Failing driving test four times.
The state of the inside of my car.
Stabbing maths textbooks with biros.
Wandering off halfway through conversations.
Leaping up from desk to run around the block x 5.
Inability to recognise people I've talked to at length.
Difficulty retaining facts, figures, sequences, instructions.
Not noticing when my husband shaves off his beard.
Everything turning to blah blah blah in meetings.
Going into sexual reverie during boring exams.
Launching jammed printers across the room.
Leaving suitcases on public transport.
Forgetting where car is parked.
Parking car very, very badly.

'You wouldn't be able to be a journalist if you had ADHD,' my GP told me at my appointment. 'Children with ADHD usually drop out of school.'

That's not true, though – plenty of journalists have 'come out' as having ADHD, including two who have won Pulitzer Prizes: Katherine Ellison, for her coverage of the corrupt reign of Ferdinand and Imelda Marcos in the Philippines; and Clarence Page, for his reporting on voter fraud. Writing is the only thing that can corral my thoughts, and excelling at it at school allowed me to bluff other subjects I struggled to listen along to.

One referral later, I was at a specialist clinic in Melbourne, undergoing the screening process. There was a slew of questionnaires. Among those, one looked like it was checking that I wasn't a psychopath. Another weeded out signs of depression. The psychologist then interviewed my husband. As the extent of my most-annoying traits occurred to him en masse, we ended up having quite the difficult few weeks. Then the verdict came: I was in the club! The diagnosis felt comforting, because everything clicked into place. I was a disorder. For a while, at least, I didn't mind that simple idea.

But now I had a quandary. Given my previous dependency on speed, should I accept the standard prescription for ADHD of the same? Even though the risk of Dexedrine, Adderall or Ritalin being a gateway to further stimulant use has no concrete studies to support it (which a cynic might argue is due to research often being funded by pharmaceutical companies), there's plenty of anecdotal evidence of abuse and dependence.

How could I ignore stories I'd heard during the research of this book, such as that of Lynne Randell, the 1970s pop star whose addiction to methamphetamine diet pills drove her to suicide in 2007? In an interview with the *Age*, three years before she died, she confessed her adrenal glands were atrophied to about thirty per cent function by that stimulant. In fact, ADHD drugs such as Ritalin were widely prescribed in Sweden as weight-loss aids before being withdrawn in the late 1960s because of abuse.

Or Harriet Wran, the daughter of former NSW premier Neville Wran, whose teenage prescription for Ritalin was raised by her defence team during prosecution for her role in the death of an ice dealer. It was when she came off the medication that she started abusing illicit drugs, they noted.

Or Elizabeth Wurtzel, the Gen-X poster child who followed up her doleful memoir *Prozac Nation* with *More, Now, Again*, about snorting forty Ritalin pills a day. Ditto Cat Marnell, the *Condé Nast* beauty editor whose ADHD medication managed her weight loss as a happy bonus, but also led to angel dust and smack, as detailed in her warp-speed memoir *How to Murder Your Life*.

Or Perth's Claire Murray, who was prescribed a daily forty-milligram dose of dexamphetamine as a twelve-year-old. During Murray's adolescence, Western Australia's prescribing rates of ADHD medications to kids climbed to three times that of the national average. By twenty-four – after two liver transplants – she was dead from her speed and heroin use. Her worthiness for receiving the second liver transplant was widely debated in the media, with *60 Minutes* asking, 'Here's the dilemma. Do we let Claire die or do we give her another chance? And who should foot the bill?' Yet a few years later, in 2015, Western Australia experienced a rebound of prescribing rates, including 8000 children, up ten per cent from the year before.

For me to ignore all these warnings would be incredibly arrogant. And, frankly, the fact that I used to sometimes buy some kind stranger's ADHD medication from a drug dealer wasn't a great sign I'd be sensible, either.

A month passed before my next appointment, which was with the prescribing psychiatrist, a snip at $650 for an assessment. I arrived twenty minutes late and without the benefit of a comb. While this wasn't deliberate, I couldn't have been more convincing. He interviewed me for ninety minutes. I still seemed to have ADHD.

The psychiatrist impassively walked me through my life history. He wondered why I hadn't reported the child sex abuse to the police. Requested to see self-harm scars. Asked if the tattoos were more of the same. *Moderate severity complicated by complex trauma and polysubstance abuse now largely in remission*, he typed.

'Give your parents a hard time?' More of a statement than a question.

He cracked a smile when he enquired about coordination, and I confessed that my headmistress at primary school had sent a note home asking if I might be slightly spastic. There was a big bruise on my knee right there in the interview, to back that up.

The assessment was long and draining. I drummed my fingers and flopped around in my seat. *Well-looking woman, fidgety and inattentive but otherwise well spoken, intelligent and articulate*, he typed.

He got to the part of the questionnaire I'd just filled in that queried current drug use and circled it. Looked up.

'I've been buying modafinil off the internet,' I said. It had been powering my writing – including of this book – ever since I read about an author with multiple sclerosis using it to sharpen her foggy brain. It seemed to have the same positive effects for me that speed once did, minus the comedown.

Modafinil is a wakefulness-promoting agent – or 'eugeroic' – commonly used to treat narcolepsy, although it's also used to treat those in methamphetamine withdrawal who suffer brain impairment. It stimulates norepinephrine (which mobilises the brain and body for action, helps with memory retrieval, and focuses the attention) and histamine, and generates greater dopamine activity in the brain. Unlike ADHD stimulants there's no euphoric element and it's thought to have no-to-low addiction risk (although manufacturers often say that, until evidence causes them to backtrack).

'Why didn't you just get a prescription?'

'I didn't know I could.'

'I can prescribe it.'

I fished the pack out of my bag, navigating a tube of exploded toothpaste. The psychiatrist was very interested in how much I'd been paying the internet merchant. He could prescribe it to me for a quarter of the strength and thrice the price. That's because it's not part of Australia's Pharmaceutical Benefits Scheme, and so isn't subsidised; which is a bit odd, since it can't be abused in the way that the much cheaper, subsidised ADHD medications can.

'But it would be the same cost as your three daily coffees,' he said, in response to my facial expression. 'Would you still need to drink them?'

'I suppose not.' I sighed, waving goodbye to another of life's great pleasures. (Joking. Of course I drink them, too.)

We agreed, at my prompting, that modafinil would be a better choice for me than prescribing a former speed fan a stimulant.

'Would Dexedrine have been a problem?' I asked.

'It depends. Do you think a heroin addict shouldn't have Panadeine because it contains an opioid?' he countered, before trotting out the argument that there's no evidence-based link between ADHD medication and illicit drug abuse.

Which is an odd thing for a psychiatrist to say, because the medication literature itself warns of a link. GlaxoSmithKline's

Dexedrine bears the following warning in capitals in its prescribing information: *AMPHETAMINES HAVE A HIGH POTENTIAL FOR ABUSE. ADMINISTRATION OF AMPHETAMINES FOR PROLONGED PERIODS OF TIME MAY LEAD TO DRUG DEPENDENCE AND MUST BE AVOIDED.*

There was something else niggling at me. ADHD can be easily misdiagnosed, because various symptoms cross over with those of anxiety, depression, autism, OCD and bipolar disorder, not to mention the fact that unresolved trauma, early-life stress and substance use are excellent at mimicking them. It's also, in my opinion, overdiagnosed in this era of pathologising personality and the human condition. Maybe I had just really liked taking speed. Maybe modafinil wasn't really making me 'better', simply faster. Was I just gamely buying into the idea that I needed medicating?

For now, I accepted my prescription for the non-amphetamine alternative. Would being officially medicated by a psychiatrist be better for me than self-medicating? Only time would tell.

6

A CRUDE FORM OF SEDUCTION

The sugar-daddy mentoring scheme of drugs

My boyfriend's twenty-nine
Got crystal meth and a Nissan Skyline with illegal mods.
I'm sixteen in a month, the department can go get fucked.
I'll do what I want, I'm not going back to Mum.
I don't like boys my age, they don't know how to treat a lady
How to get it sideways or put it in my neck.

'Nothing That I'm Needing' by Gentle Ben
and His Sensitive Side (Spooky Records)

After I lost my first job I took a drug and alcohol course that involved a work-experience stint at a London rehab. I liked loitering around the topic of drugs, even if the slant here was abstinence but, as was a theme in my life, I didn't imagine I qualified to seek help myself. So I shadowed the residents to life-skills group and to art class, speed buzzing stealthily through my veins.

I did feel shifty working there under the influence, but I soon realised I wasn't the only one. The general manager – who, whenever he called me into his office, always seemed to be changing out of his trousers and into his gym gear, or vice versa – once pointed at the crook of my arm and laughed knowingly. He was mistaking the duskier skin tone for evidence that I was shooting up. That wasn't a problem, apparently.

My other realisation was that the female residents often wound up there through being introduced to drugs by men – or so their stories went, anyway. They seemed to be the passive victims of misguided love affairs.

I could relate to that. As a disenfranchised girl, I gravitated towards older men the way that disenfranchised boys have gravitated towards the IRA or ISIS. I was a willing pawn awaiting detonation.

It all began with Mark when I was fourteen. That year, 1989, the Berlin Wall came down and Reagan delivered his farewell address. It was the beginning of a New World Order, and I was establishing a regime of my own. I was on an active search for mentors, feeders, and suppliers: of information, experience and whatever else was on offer.

Through an advertisement I placed in the *NME* I met girls who followed my favourite band around the country. These girls gave themselves the same surname as the band. They were older than me and could check in to cheap hotels. The best I could do was bunk off school when the band was playing the next town along and go to the sound check.

I still have the journal that logs it all: the fortuitous moment that I bumped into the merchandise chick outside the venue; what she wore; what I wore; the moment my guitarist was summoned to meet me and came out of the dressing-room with a big smirk on his face; the other band members peering around the door in a cloud of smoke and then shutting it again; the exchanging of addresses when I insisted I wasn't allowed to stay for the show, which he thought was funny; the shaky inhalation of half a scrimped-and-saved cigarette alone in the smoking carriage of the train home.

Over the next six months, Mark and I wrote to each other. He was twenty-four, famous, and my escape route out of Slough. I couldn't believe my luck. When an envelope landed on the mat with my name in his crazed script, I'd sprint upstairs and open it. He wrote on the backs of tour posters, decorated with splurts of glue and paint. I kept them in a lockable vanity case, along with my amyl nitrate and menthol cigarettes.

Mark consoled me about home life, provided descriptions of the effects of various drugs, and illuminated a way of life that was pure freedom. He mailed me little lumps of cannabis resin, band T-shirts, and mixtapes. 'I'll write to your mum and tell her you're doing your homework,' he offered, when I wrote that I couldn't come to their next London show.

When I was fifteen, I was allowed to take the train to London on Saturdays, provided I was back before dark. Of course, my weekly pilgrimage was to Mark's flat. I drank all the way on the train to combat my nerves, and once there I would solemnly accept the giant bong he handed over – once he'd bubbled his way through his own hit. I couldn't deal with bongs, but neither was I likely to say no. Once primed, I'd sit in a daze, only able to watch his fingers journeying hypnotically around the fretboard of his guitar as he watched me in turn. His flat smelled of the pot plants that grew under hydroponic lights in one corner, and patchouli oil, paint, and the sharp tang of body odour – because he was always working shirtless beneath acrylic-splattered dungarees.

If I sobered up enough, Mark would teach me how to cook simple dishes like pasta with pesto and pine nuts, or he'd go into one of his rants about Thatcher. I got the feeling he saw me as a blank slate, to be indoctrinated. Sometimes we watched films: *A Clockwork Orange*, *Brazil*, *Delicatessen*, trippy fractal videos, or bootleg movies of accidental deaths and murders. Sometimes he slotted some porn into the VHS, although when he lay down right next to me on the mattress one day, I freaked out and stiffened. He just laughed and sat back up again.

When I first started going to visit Mark, I had long bleached hair with a shaved undercut, like he used to have, but in time I started gluing it into dreadlocks, like he had now. One day he said, 'I don't like it when my girlfriends try to look like me.' Was I his girlfriend?

By the time I turned sixteen I was completely in love. Sometimes we went out, like to the shops, and the sunshine burst around him in a sonic boom. The only fly in my ointment was Mark's ex-girlfriend Debbie. She'd left him for somebody else, but she was still on the scene and always interfering.

One day we were in Debbie's Mini Cooper, coming back from Portobello Market – me squeezed in the back seat – and she eavesdropped into our conversation about where I could get some speed. She scolded him, 'You shouldn't be supplying drugs to a sixteen-year-old.' But Mark was a man of non-convention, a citizen of the earth; he questioned everything, and he ordered me to question everything, too. He grinned sheepishly but later gave me a phone number anyway, which I used for the next eight years.

Back in Slough, a bit drunk, I wandered into Mum's bedroom and announced I was in love. I expected her to be angry, but instead she gave me a basil plant to give to Mark for his pesto. Better the devil you know, she probably thought. At least I'd told her. Some of it.

Between Saturdays I continued my channelling of Mark by doing things I thought he would in theory approve of, although he never did. I painted my white Stratocaster copy stripy up the fretboard, like his, although I did mine with poster paint. Once it had dried I used it – sounding a bit muted – to write the three-chord punk song 'You Make Me Sick'. That was about Debbie. I'd additionally dropped into her clothes shop one day and nicked a skirt, slipping it under my dress in the changing room as I made bright conversation with the shop assistant, then walking off with a spring in my step.

Not long after I started sleeping with Mark, I told my best friend Fiona the exciting news. She told her friend Karen, who told her friend Debbie. Within a few days I got a phone call from Mark, who spoke in a cold, tight voice I hadn't heard before. He reminded me that I wasn't supposed to tell anyone (did we agree to that? I really don't remember) and that I was to give him his bass guitar back immediately. He hung up. The following Saturday, I lugged his bass into London and took it to Debbie's shop. He accepted it, stony-faced, while Debbie discreetly busied herself at a clothes rack. If she'd made the connection that the plaster-cast vulva in Mark's latest artwork was mine, she wasn't going to make an issue about it. I hesitated there on the shop floor, then moped back to suburbia.

Women have the definite advantage when it comes to procuring drugs. You're not going to find a listings advert like this – *Girls take these drugs off my hands pls: no drama just come have some and enjoy get shouted and its a good thing i can host in south melb if you need or i'll travel* – with the gender roles reversed.

That was a real ad from *Craigslist*. It was flagged and taken down, but these offers pop up on similar sites all the time. (Tip: if something seems too good to be true, it definitely is.)

For a less chilling example, few presentable young women will get knocked back if they ask for a line of cocaine from a man within their group. Not if they ask nicely. But it's when this kind of bartering – of being 'nice' for drugs – becomes a regular and escalating exchange that there's a steady erosion of wellbeing.

Dr Jennifer Johnston is a research fellow at the University Centre for Rural Health in Lismore. There, she oversees the collection of data on different aspects of drug use in the region, spanning the remote towns between Tweed Heads and Grafton. With unemployment and homelessness high in the region, manufacturing and distributing meth can provide an opportunity for income, with men controlling the flow. And where the men flow, the women follow. Sometimes it's the status of a dealer that is alluring to a young woman; other times the subsidised lifestyle may be the main appeal, particularly in communities that offer few rewards.

'The girls may have dropped out of school and then there's little else to do,' Johnston tells me. 'At the start, drug use is social and it's fun. On paper, ice sounds amazing: a sense of euphoria, optimism, energy. If you haven't been previously feeling any of those things, that's powerful.'

As Johnston explains it to me, 'The girls start using meth because these guys have good access to it. Then the girls become dependent on the meth and reliant on the guy. The relationship turns sour. There's often a lot of domestic violence, or they owe the guy – or his friends – sexual favours. The girls can't get out, so they end up being violent themselves, then the cops get involved and the girls are saying, "You've got to get me out of here." They can't see a way out.'

In the nearby town of Casino, which police call the ice capital of the Northern Rivers, one female resident told the local paper, 'I was nineteen and my partner at the time, who was eleven years older than me, was selling ice.' She describes him injecting her one of the first times she used it, rather than easing into it gently by snorting or smoking. 'I reckon he got me on it so I would lose weight,' she says.

In those cases where men are obtaining, paying for, and injecting the drugs, there's an imbalance of labour that then establishes an imbalance of power. Women will probably borrow needles and ancillary equipment from these men, and so are at more risk of acquiring blood-borne diseases because they're often at the bottom of drug-circle hierarchies. They're last in the queue for needles, perhaps because they're not injecting themselves, or because they're receiving a fix for free.

Geoff Corbett is a senior clinician who works with young adults in Brisbane. He tells me that women will often willingly go second on their partner's needle because of a misguided sense of romance – which ties in with numerous studies that report that the progression by women to injecting drugs often stems from a desire to increase commitment and intimacy within a romantic partnership. 'It's no different to the vast majority of the population when in a relationship,' he says. 'They want to feel trusted. A way of demonstrating trust in a drug relationship is, "Look, we share needles because we trust each other." Unfortunately, trust isn't able to screen for blood-borne viruses.'

In 1992 I was seventeen. Andrew Morton published *Diana: Her True Story.* Three lots of royals split up. Windsor Castle – close to the college where I was doing Year 11 and 12 – caught fire. It was the Queen's annus horribilis, and not that great for me either.

After a hiatus I was allowed to see Mark again, but neither of us raised the idea of resuming the sex. Instead, I suggested he introduce me to one of his friends; be a broker, if you will. My diary bore lists of things a girl needed to do to complete her education, such as use handcuffs (not furry ones), dress up, anoint oils, perfect a blowjob. I was pretty anxious about not having nailed it all and of lagging behind my peers. It was yet another way in which an older man could be useful; and yes, I was probably trying to get back at Mark.

Mark floated the idea to his mate Martin, a thirty-six-year-old sculptor who was quite debonair, and in and out of rehab for coke addiction. He reported back that Martin was keen. I still only had Saturday daytimes to work with – having to be back in Slough in time for dinner.

The first time we met, we went for a picnic, to which I contributed a can of Strongbow. Martin brought a blanket and sweated all over it because he was withdrawing from cocaine again. I wasn't a very good conversationalist, so he talked at length about a nymphomaniac he used to date who used to dress in trouser suits and carry a long black cigarette holder. I thought this sounded a bit pretentious, but at some point I did buy a cigarette holder of my own.

I can only remember what Martin looked like because he gave me a strip of arty black-and-white passport photos to study. We saw each other at his flat for about six weeks of Saturdays, but I can't remember any of it, nor much of the flat itself, because I'd have to get drunk so that I could deal with the sex I'd procured him to have.

I may not have been logging the details myself, but someone else was. Martin had a friend who was a newspaper columnist, the kind who serialised his own private life and that of his cohorts. The columnist took to detailing the curious case of the sculptor and the teenage girl, as though it were some decadent bohemian adventure. I started to wonder seriously if I should charge Martin for services rendered.

I decided the adventure was over when Martin went off to rehab again – a fantastically expensive joint in the country. He took to ringing me at my parents' house, sounding like a petulant child. I'd pull the cord halfway up the stairs and speak low. Rehab can bring on a disempowering feeling, initially anyway, with everything that defines the individual and gives them worth being stripped away. As Martin described the ways in which he and the fellow residents were banding together to rebel against the staff, even his voice sounded weaker.

Perhaps there was a small window in Martin's twenties in which a spell in rehab would have been an exotic rite of passage. At thirty-six, he was ailing, and not even in a position to provide me with the cocaine he kept talking about. That was the thing about jonesing for older men: you always got there too late.

The lyrics that open this chapter are written by Brisbane musician Ben Corbett (brother of clinician Geoff, whom you met earlier), who was himself once a drug and alcohol counsellor. They're case notes based on stories he'd hear every day, the surly responses of an adolescent girl who admits that her boyfriend, thirteen years her senior, injects her in the neck.

The first time he did that he probably told her that her veins were no good and offered to find a sweet spot, gently stroking her hair out of the way. Think of the scene in the movie *Animal Kingdom*, when Ben Mendelsohn's character Pope persuades a teenage girl to try smack. He leaps forward with the needle before she's had time to weigh it up. 'It's fun. Go ahead, come on, put your arm out,' he says in a steady murmur, a reassuring uncle. 'That's it. There we go.'

These are the kinds of tales I've heard, in brief and in passing, that have led to seasoned counsellors taking sick leave. Like that of the drug-dependent sex worker being injected in the neck with a substance unknown, without her consent. Or the teenage girl meeting older guys on sugar-daddy websites. She'd be flown interstate and given drugs and money in return for sex, until her looks went and, with it, her ability to score.

Yet outside of studies of sex-workers I've found little research to support the idea that the female route into drugs can be through a predatory older male. Geoff Corbett tells me: 'We know anecdotally this stuff happens all the time, and there have been libraries full of research written from a feminist perspective, yet there's a paucity of data to support this.' He hardly needs to add, 'It's something that needs to be looked at.'

Dr James Rowe is a researcher at RMIT who has led longitudinal studies into the lives of St Kilda sex workers, and the stories he's collected from women about their introduction to heroin *before* falling into sex work can at least shed light on this under-researched area. (We might assume that this power dynamic also applies to other substances that require initiation, such as shooting meth or smoking crack.)

In his 2011 report for Victoria's Inner South Community Health Service, titled *Surveying HIV and Need in the Unregulated Sex Industry*, there's a section titled 'Exploitation'. In it, he notes: 'A number of interviewees told of being introduced to heroin by former or current partners. In some cases, this was a process initiated by a man seizing an opportunity to exploit vulnerable young women that has led to not only drug dependency but also a loss of self-respect and dignity. For the relative security of a male who offers protection and sometimes shelter, the women, in return, agree to sex work as a means of earning sufficient income to pay not only for their own needs but for the drugs of the men whose actions may have led them to this very precarious existence. Once in this position, it can become very difficult to extricate themselves from what turns from an outwardly respectful and caring relationship to one characterised by abuse and exploitation.'

1993. Princess Diana withdrew from public life. I'd made my own newspaper headlines, thanks to *Slapper*, and was in my first year at university. Dad recently examined a photograph of me taken that year. I'm sat on the hall stairs, on the phone, winding the curly lead around one hand. My hair is hacked and black, my skirt similarly shorn and trailing threads.

'It could have gone either way then,' Dad mused, reclining in a patio chair, the lunch plates clean but for crumbs.

'What could have?'

'Your mental health.'

I don't know which way he thinks it went but I'm pretty sure it went the other.

That year Mark introduced me to Christian, who was addicted to freebase cocaine, which he preferred because it's purer than crack, although sometimes we smoked that, too. I wasn't a fan of the stuff, but I had a hard time saying no to things. Within seconds of each hit I became as rigid as a coathanger. Over time, my mouth grew stiff and sore.

Christian had a three-storey apartment right by the Portobello Market. I never established how he could afford such dizzying prime real estate because he was evasive with the truth. He told me he was the original Johnnie Fingers in the Boomtown Rats. Later he said he was once the bloke out of Scarlet Fantastic. He was neither. I still don't know who he was.

He was always charming, though, not like Mark or Martin. 'We want you to be comfortable,' he would say, arranging cushions, loading pipes, putting on the films of my choice. He got mini-cab drivers to deliver pastries for me, packets of cigarettes, and pizza. He never ate anything himself. Sex wasn't a possibility, though he liked us to sit around naked; preferably on the floor, so that we could comb for crumbs. I didn't know what he used to look like, but now he was painfully thin, bruising every time he sat down in the jacuzzi. He was probably in his forties but looked ten years older, at least.

Sometimes Mark came around for a chat and a smoke, but he didn't stay long. When he'd see me there, he'd ask if I was okay and try to smile, but it would freeze on his face in a grimace. It was as if he knew his social experiment with the blank slate had gone too far somehow. He was now in an adult relationship with an eco-hippy called Bex, who was cordial with me but didn't engage.

Increasingly, mysterious women buzzed the intercom and wailed up at Christian's windows, throwing stones. He pretended not to notice. Mark said they were probably prostitutes. After three months, Christian bored of me and ignored my intercom buzzes, too. It was just in the nick of time, because I was not yet dependent on crack or freebase, but for the next year the taste and smell of it would hit me whenever I ran a bubble bath or the sun came out. Some of my university coursework was on Christian's computer, but I never got it back because he never again answered his phone.

Years later, I heard that, whoever Christian was, a group of men burst into his flat one day and cleared out all his furniture as he sat there smoking. The royalties must have run out.

Just how passive was I? I'd had a fascination with drugs since starting high school and checking out as many library books on the subject as I could. A few years later I realised it took older men to facilitate the deal. Clever me.

While writing this chapter, which causes me more stomach-churning unease than any other, I find a 2007 paper titled 'The gendered context of initiation to injecting drug use: evidence for women as active initiates'. The clue's in the title – women aren't always as passive as we imagine.

I contact one of its authors, Dr Joanne Bryant, who is a senior research fellow at the Centre for Social Research in Health at the University of New South Wales. She and Professor Carla Treloar have collected data from 334 people who inject drugs in New South Wales and Queensland. They found that, of the females, actually only about a third were initiated by sexual partners. The others either injected themselves or were initiated by friends.

'Many women have agency over their drug use,' Dr Bryant tells me. 'It's true that there are times when women feel pressured to inject drugs, but there is also research evidence that the people who give the injections feel pressured into giving them.'

Dr Bryant cites a 1998 study by Rhodes and Quirk, in which some women described how their male partner's drug use was part of the attraction. Those researchers deduced that young women were using drugs to bolster their ideas of equality and of being the 'same as men', just as I associated alcohol with being on the 'winning team'. Personally, I liked the idea of actively seeking out my mentors. And wasn't I engaging in symbiotic relationships, a trade-off of resources?

Clinician Geoff Corbett tells me: 'Often it's up to the spectator to determine whether there's a power imbalance, and that all depends on where their belief system lies.' Incidentally, this chapter's title, 'a crude form of seduction', is a phrase I nicked from Corbett, which he uses to describe the dynamic between older men and teenage girls in drug-taking scenarios.

According to Corbett: 'The younger person might explain to me, "Well, actually I'm exploiting them – I get all these drugs for free." And then I'm like, "Yes, but you're also having sex with them." "Yes, but that doesn't cost me anything." "Yes, but if we were to put a price on the sex that you're performing – the same as we do for drugs – what's the going rate for oral sex from a sixteen-year-old girl?"

'We don't actually talk like that to clients,' he clarifies, 'but part of my job is to get them to realise it's not a free ride and that there are definite costs involved to what they're engaging in. It's cumulative and it affects their sense of self-worth, especially when they attenuate their perspective to what their self-worth is in dollars and cents. Even if you're just being an economic rationalist, they're being ripped off.'

Corbett says that such women tend to have already experienced some form of neglect or abuse and so are more vulnerable to that sort of dynamic. 'That older male role is often perceived as a charismatic, protective figure, no matter how much abuse is doled out,' he says. 'I hear, "They give me drugs for free, who else would do that?" "Their drugs are the best drugs." "If it's not them that's using me it will be someone else." They're probably right, but it's also inherently morally wrong.'

Of course there were other men, in my game of who's-exploiting-whom. Such as the ex-con coke dealer who wrote earnest songs on his acoustic guitar about young men going off to war, and whose life was so alien to me that even as a teenager I had the good grace to feel sheepish about my holiday in it. And the poly-user (more's the fun) whose room was completely bare but for one photo of himself tacked to the back of his door. He once held my head under water in the bathroom sink, something I only remembered when writing this book. And the speed dealer whose number Mark gave me all those years ago, who I never slept with, but who recently contacted me on Facebook to demand why not.

I prided myself on rolling with the punches and testing my mettle. If my life was an experiment, these men were just uncontrolled variables. I had always considered my blazing nosedives through their lives to be the daring adventures of youth. No harm done.

All the same, as the years went on, I never allowed myself to think about them.

7

PRETTY INTENSE

Promiscuity, borderline personality disorder and other labels that only come in pink

Béatrice Dalle in *Betty Blue* is the poster girl for borderline personality disorder. She was pinned up on student walls the world over in the late 1980s and early 1990s; often by the sorts of men who were always complaining about being harassed by crazy women, or by the sort of women who had become resigned to that sort of classification.

A Betty is fun at first. She's the volatile woman on the cover of pulp novels who smokes reefers, brandishes flick-knives, and gets her blouse torn off. She has kohl-smudged eyes, a great home-hacked fringe, swigs whisky from the bottle, wears artfully trashy underwear, and drops her ash in the bedsheets, occasionally setting fire to the house.

But she becomes a drag. She suffers mood swings, obsessive thoughts, and violent outbursts. Look closer and there's a litany of fine lines up her arms from broken wine glasses and razor blades. Her drug use spirals out of control, and the sex becomes stalky. She's an attention-seeker, a drama queen, a chaos merchant, a slut.

She's the kiss-and-tell mistress. She's the girl who stitches up defenceless football coaches. Maybe, briefly, someone with a Betty fetish will try to fix her, but eventually she just becomes another crazy-bitch anecdote.

Men can be diagnosed, too, but BPD has come to represent a certain type of woman in the public psyche: Winona Ryder in *Girl, Interrupted*; Demi Moore in *St Elmo's Fire*; Uma Thurman in *Pulp Fiction*; Jennifer Jason Leigh in *Single White Female*; Emily Lloyd in *Wish You Were Here*; Vivien Leigh in *Gone with the Wind*. At least, these are the characters that the armchair experts of the internet have diagnosed in forums over the years. In short, BPD has become the buzz term for unruly females.

Thing is, it's a construct. While BPD has been pathologised in the *Diagnostic and Statistical Manual of Mental Disorders* as a disorder – with a three-to-one female-to-male ratio – it's more accurately a suite of coping mechanisms. Its behind-the-scenes nickname, in fact, is 'hard-life syndrome'.

In her book *Cognitive-Behavioral Treatment of Borderline Personality Disorder*, Marsha Linehan cites various studies of BPD patients to conclude that sixty-seven per cent to eighty-six per cent had experienced childhood sexual abuse. Other common drivers are neglect, a break in parental bond, and witnessing violence or abuse. To be diagnosed, an individual needs to meet five out of nine criteria that include: frantic efforts to avoid real or imagined abandonment; unstable interpersonal relationships; unstable self-image; impulsivity; suicidal behaviour or self-harm; reactive moods; chronic feelings of emptiness; difficulty controlling anger; and paranoia or dissociation.

How do you reckon people deal with those kinds of feelings? That's right! Self-medication. Two-thirds of people with BPD will develop problematic use of substances at some point in their lives, making it the personality disorder with the second-highest substance use prevalence, after the more male-associated antisocial personality disorder.

So is it time to ditch the label? Professor Jayashri Kulkarni thinks so. She's the director of the Monash Alfred Psychiatry Research Centre in Melbourne.

'The term "borderline personality disorder" is derogatory,' she tells me emphatically. 'It demeans everything. It loses the connection with the early trauma, whereas at least if you call it "complex trauma disorder", as we do here, you force clinicians to think, "Hang on, did I ask about that?" The consumers are catching on to that term, but to get it catching on more widely I feel as though we need campaign buttons.'

It's a sentiment echoed by Professor Jane Ussher from the Centre for Health Research at Western Sydney University. 'Some people have described BPD as a dustbin diagnosis,' she says. 'Women who are "difficult" or resistant might be diagnosed as borderline today. If you look at a woman's history and she has experienced sexual or physical abuse, calling her "borderline" pathologises it. It says to women they've got an illness, rather than their reaction is understandable.'

Ussher thinks having a historical perspective is important when considering this pathologisation of women. In the nineteenth century, inconvenient women could be committed to asylums by their husbands for reasons such as postnatal depression, or being infertile, or simply to make way for a new affair. It would take one doctor's signature to have a woman committed, but three signatures for her to win her freedom – an impossibility.

'Women have always been positioned as mad,' Ussher says. 'What we can see historically is women who step outside the boundaries of idealised femininity are given a label. It's a way of regulating women – if you cross that boundary there are going to be consequences in how you're going to be seen, how you're going to be treated.'

What additionally fires Ussher up is that there's a profit to be made in making BPD a diagnostic classification. According to the research of Dr Marcia Angell, writing for the *New York Review of Books* in 2011, about one-fifth of the funding of the American Psychiatric Association – which puts out the *DSM* – comes from pharmaceutical companies, and more than half of all *DSM-5* taskforce members have significant industry interests. Ussher explains, 'We've got a circular problem here. It's the American Psychiatric Association that devises all these diagnostic categories and creates new ones every time they have a new *DSM*. They decide the symptoms, from which people – primarily women – are diagnosed, which then creates a market for these drugs.'

There's also a gender bias to take into consideration. Marcie Kaplan noted in a 1983 article in *American Psychologist* that the experts on the *DSM* taskforce were mostly men who had codified their biased assumptions about what behaviours were healthy in a woman and what were not. And seven years later, in his book *Sex Differences: Modern Biology and the Unisex Fallacy*, veteran biologist Yves Christen called the *DSM* 'a masterful piece of sexism: it takes gender into consideration, in that its definitions of psychological normality differ for men and women'.

All of this doesn't bode well for the woman seeking professional help. Professor Kulkarni describes stories she's heard of women being traumatised further by going to the emergency department after a suicide attempt and being treated badly. 'This is a patient who will present sometimes with mania, sometimes depression, sometimes dissociation, sometimes with brief psychotic episodes,' she says. 'On the one hand, this is a very difficult person to manage; on the other hand, the health services are not looking for the whole story. Doctors and mental health services only see the end product: "Here's the nineteen-year-old who's turned up yet again with a drug overdose or Panadol overdose, wasting our time. Is she really trying to kill herself? Well, why the hell doesn't she do it properly?"'

One significant problem for doctors is that there are 256 different presentations of BPD – because there are that many combinations of the diagnostic criteria. No wonder it's easier to put a patient on medication and move on – or maybe five different medications. 'They get an antipsychotic, an antidepressant, a mood stabiliser, a benzodiazepine tranquilliser, then they might be doing their own drugs and alcohol,' says Kulkarni, 'and it's a bloody debacle because each of those has side effects. Think about the intermittent disruption to the brain – the biochemistry and circuitry. Then there are the intermittent stresses that will disrupt everything, and then there are substances that will trigger everything. By the time someone thinks, hang on, maybe there was something in their early life that we should be dealing with in a psychotherapeutic sense, the person is in a complete mess.'

The good news is that Professor Ussher believes that, unlike some disorders, BPD certainly need not be a lifetime companion. 'Say I had a diagnosis of BPD,' she says, 'in five years' time I might not be exhibiting those behaviours, and that might be for a whole range of reasons. I might have had good therapy and learned healthy coping mechanisms. My living situation might have changed. I might have got in a really good relationship – we know that positive relationships are a really good protector of mental health, for both men and women. What we know for sure is that the greatest "cure" for a whole range of psychological disorders is time. Time is the greatest healer.'

My radar swivelled when I read an interview in *Elle* with American pop star Halsey, whose image, lyrics and hair all pop in glorious technicolour. She lives with bipolar disorder, and she was discussing the way in which some people fetishise women with mental health issues.

'They're like, "I want to be with someone who is like crazy." Well, guess what? It's not all painting at four o'clock in the morning and road trips and fucking great things,' she said. 'Sometimes it's throwing things and, like, getting hurt and having to pick someone up from the police station at two o'clock in the morning. My biggest fear has always been being that woman.'

When I interviewed her for *Rolling Stone*, she added, 'I was what certain people would call a "promiscuous" girl in high school, which is a shitty word – I hate that.'

Impulsive sexual behaviour is common during the manic periods of bipolar disorder, and also in borderline personality disorder, but it's more likely to be pathologised in female patients and overlooked as normal in men.

Professor Ussher thinks the term 'promiscuity' is as bunk as BPD. 'For women, promiscuity is both a symptom of madness and a value judgement,' she says. 'The actress Frances Farmer is a good example. In the 1940s [as some accounts have it] she had a lobotomy at the behest of her mother because she was promiscuous, as her mother described it. Today that behaviour would be seen as completely normal, but she was given a diagnosis of madness.'

'Promiscuity' seems to imply moral failing and mental weakness, although the Oxford English Dictionary defines it simply as: 'characterised by many transient sexual relationships'. It isn't listed in the *DSM*, yet it's casually applied to women, or gay men, in such a diagnostic way, as though their sexuality is threatening or clinically abnormal. A straight man who sleeps around is less likely to earn a label, although in extreme cases he might be given the more carnivorous 'sex addict'.

There are studies that suggest that females reporting casual sex acknowledge more depressive symptoms than males. Some of that might be attributed to trying to avoid stigma, but sometimes there might also be an element of what Freud called repetition compulsion: unconscious adult re-enactment of a cycle of seeking attention from a caregiver as a child and being rejected.

In her book *Loose Girl: A Memoir of Promiscuity*, Kerry Cohen acknowledges that a lack of attention at home as an eleven-year-old, combined with the realisation that her body was starting to attract attention, launched an adolescence of bar-hopping and the daring seduction of older men. It's a pattern echoed in Kathy Dobie's memoir *The Only Girl in the Car*, in which the teenage Kathy is turned on by risk-taking and a new sense of power – rather than by sex itself.

Sometimes these habits can come down to self-retraumatisation. According to Professor Kulkarni, a woman locked into this grim kind of groundhog day is experiencing the residual rage of early-life trauma. 'The deliberate self-harm of addictions, or the self-harm of being involved in harmful relationships are all expressions of rage taken inwards, and of really poor self-esteem,' she says. 'The person will often have a constant barrage of negative self-talk.'

There must be a certain kind of comfort in repeating behaviour that is familiar, I suggest, even if that behaviour causes further stresses.

'Exactly,' Kulkarni says. 'That also predisposes a person to the attitude: "Look, see, of course that was going to happen to me." There's a masochistic self-fulfilment of the prophecy: "I don't deserve anything good." Hence she gets involved with the worst kind of relationship.'

In case you were wondering, an addiction story doesn't necessarily involve trauma. Many of the addiction memoirs I've read don't reference childhood trauma at all; in any case, it's likely the messages we receive as children do more damage than any incidents themselves. But to flip that into reverse, it's rare for a trauma story not to involve addiction.

What I'm surprised to learn is that there's a physiological component to trauma. Biologically, a girl who experiences it in early life will undergo significant changes in her body and brain. There's a massive rise in the stress hormone cortisol, which triggers a whole chain of reactions.

'It sets off changes in her reproductive hormone system, so that there's often a large number of women who have problems with weight or develop diabetes, polycystic ovarian syndrome and infertility,' says Kulkarni, 'but it also affects the glutamate system in the brain, which leads to difficulties in learning new information, and with cognitive changes that leads to poor self-esteem and self-harm. Then you have an effect on the amygdala, which leads to things like rage. Her biological systems are set at a sensitive threshold and she doesn't have the usual biochemistry that lets her be resilient in the face of the next trauma and the next trauma.'

Cumulative trauma makes it harder to care about oneself and, if it's harder to care, fewer precautions will be taken and so on. As well as adding multiple layers of stress and negative self-belief to the body and psyche, these re-enacting behaviours – such as having sex with abusive partners – can trigger post-traumatic stress disorder (PTSD) relating back to the early-life incident. Because of that high level of cortisol in the brain, the individual becomes hypervigilant and sensitive to triggers that remind them of the incident, be that a visual cue, a sound, or a smell.

PTSD is most likely to occur in those who have a genetic vulnerability to anxiety or depression, or in those who have experienced a previous trauma, such as war, sexual assault, road accidents, or other threats to their life. The classification was coined in the 1980s, mainly in response to the research that was going on around Vietnam War veterans, and the flashbacks and physical symptoms of anxiety they suffered. Going further back, around the First World War, it was known as shell shock.

It's a condition that's frequently self-medicated with stupefying substances, such as alcohol, cannabis, heroin and benzodiazepines. Actually, substance-abusing populations present with rates of PTSD at about five times that of the general population.

That's where someone like Lisa Kunde comes in. She's a registered psychologist in Brisbane who has assessed patients with PTSD, and she explains to me the similarities in cases between those people we have long associated with the disorder – war veterans – and people who have experienced sexual trauma.

'Often people who are drawn to the military in the first place have experienced early-life stress or family dysfunction,' she says. 'What they're seeking by joining the defence force is their "family", a sense of meaning, purpose and belonging not previously experienced as a young person. Then their identity and sense of the world gets shattered if they return home and struggle to relate with their partners, children and friends.'

It's a similar deal with sexual abuse, she argues. 'It's that moment your identity is shattered. And your family dynamic has now completely changed. Also, with those people, their relationship with their own body has been changed.'

Whereas men often externalise stress, it's more common for women to self-harm or become locked into abusive relationships.

'The brain works to protect us so that we can keep on going,' says Kunde. 'For those people who can't remember an event, they've usually learned a coping strategy to deal with it. Some people disassociate. It gives a place of safety, an escape from the external environment and the internal distress.'

I think back to a clinician telling me about having to take stress leave after hearing a horrific rape story from a client. She'd told him the details on autopilot, as though she were narrating the plot of a boring movie. He'd experienced countertransference, absorbing the emotions that were absent in her.

'Someone who's disassociated will feel like they're no longer in their body,' Kunde elaborates. 'They're outside, looking down on the situation. Stress is also a really big trigger, feeling like they're not in control.'

When it comes to treating a person who has concurrent substance dependence and PTSD, Kunde says, 'You work on the alcohol and drugs first, talking about the pros and cons of use, because usually the pros tie in to how they sleep better or feel better. Then we'll explore the emotions, feelings and thoughts associated with PTSD and how the drugs are being used to manage those. Anger is a big one, but shame is the really scary one, because that's the one that can tip people over and cause them to eradicate themselves. The drugs only help in the short term – in the long term, the symptoms of PTSD are perpetuated.'

While a suitable treatment option might be trauma-focused therapy, it's looking possible that, by 2021, MDMA could be legalised for therapeutic treatment of PTSD. MDMA (also known as ecstasy) triggers the release of large amounts of serotonin and dopamine as well as the 'cuddle chemical' oxytocin. Together, these chemicals create a mental landscape of connection and acceptance.

An early recipient of this psychotherapy, 'Rachel', took part in an FDA-approved clinical trial through the Multidisciplinary Association for Psychedelic Studies (MAPS) and has become a strong advocate. 'You get the value and it lasts,' she told US talk show *The Doctors*. 'In my case it took three sessions and that did the trick.' Unlike self-medication, which tends to be an unofficial program of maintenance (so regular that dependence becomes a risk), using psychedelics and MDMA for personal growth is a much more mindful experience.

Melissa Warner, co-founder of the Australian Psychedelic Society and herself someone who has sought treatment for PTSD, welcomes this progress. 'I actually have a philosophical opposition to using drugs as an escape,' Warner says. 'I embrace difficulty and challenge as a pathway to growth.' As Warner explains it, our memory is more like an editable Word document than it is a printed page. 'Memories aren't just written once but every time we remember them. Remembering creates a critical window, during which your state at the time can alter the original memory. The curse of PTSD is that when a traumatic memory is remembered it produces fear, re-encoding the memory with greater trauma.'

In an attempt to combat this, conventional therapy sessions might involve the client visualising themselves in a safe place before recalling a trauma – but even so, the client's 'window of tolerance' tends to be narrow. The idea of using MDMA is that the traumatic memory is encoded with self-love and empathy, diminishing future re-experiences of trauma. To that end, if MDMA is prescribed for therapeutic use, it will only be administered by trained psychotherapists.

Whatever the method used to treat it, trauma can be reframed as a transformative experience. That's known as post-traumatic growth, and it's a shift in thinking that stems from a personal challenge and leads to a positive transformation of character. There's an alteration of perspective and a switching of priorities; a desire to not sweat the small stuff. Some relationships are culled, others are strengthened. New philosophies are ushered in, such as changing career to pursue more meaningful work. But all this requires commitment. A key component is 'sense-making': the ability to envisage a negative situation as having a positive outcome. If low resilience is a risk-factor for substance dependence – as outlined in chapter one – by the same token, learning resilience is vital for sense-making.

Of course, post-traumatic growth is only likely to occur if there's a lifestyle change; if an individual's decision-making is still resulting in cumulative trauma, they're unlikely to experience an epiphany. Some kind of agent for change is needed, be it seeking professional help or tackling problematic substance use.

Australia's Blue Knot Foundation (formerly known as Adults Surviving Child Abuse) offers trauma practice guidelines to clinicians, and trauma-informed care is already in place in some drug and alcohol services. The challenge is to get all health professionals, including GPs and emergency doctors, to recognise trauma and take it seriously.

Tangentially, an additional challenge would be to encourage people not to misuse the term PTSD, which has had its definition watered down in recent years from 'witnessing or experiencing a terrifying event that endangered the life or safety of the individual or others', to 'bullied at work', 'stress', or 'anxiety'. It's become as ubiquitous as 'nervous breakdown' was among my school friends in the 1980s, and is in danger of being a catchcry of systematic victimisation, rather than a disorder with specific criteria.

8

COLLATERAL DAMAGE

Blacking out, passing out, spiking . . . and the opportunists who dig it

You never regain the memory of what has happened in a blackout, quite simply because you never committed the event to short-term memory in the first place. A large quantity of grog can block the NMDA receptors in the hippocampus. These transmit glutamate, which carries signals between neurons, and blocking them prevents formation of memory. A person in a blackout could be wandering along train tracks and notice a train is coming, but lack the subsequent synaptic connections needed to register and take action. It's like you're swinging from vine to vine of awareness and when you look behind you there's nothing there anymore.

'Behold the risk factors for blacking out,' writes journalist Sarah Hepola in her memoir *Blackout: Remembering the Things I Drank to Forget*: 'a genetic predisposition to holding your liquor, drinking fast, and skipping meals. Oh, and one more: being female.'

Males and females process substances very differently. It's not just down to the most visible disparity: body mass. More alcohol enters a female's bloodstream and body water because of lower concentrations of the dehydrogenase enzyme, which metabolises alcohol in the stomach. Females also generally have lower body-water content, and consequently the effects of alcohol – or any other drug – are not as diluted. This is exacerbated by having a lower muscle-to-fat ratio than males; blood flows through muscle tissue, but not so much through fat, which further means that alcohol is less diluted in a female's body. As a consequence of all these factors, a woman might believe she is driving under the limit but have actually exceeded the legal blood-alcohol-content level. She's also more prone to brownouts (that's fragmentary loss of memory) and blackouts, beaming up to that malevolent mothership.

Rematerialise in 1993: I was eighteen and my life was a science experiment, there to be trifled with. There was no such thing as a bad experience, only experience itself.

For the previous two years I'd been going to Reading Festival with friends and a tent. Reading was an annual pilgrimage for southern kids, who would disembark from the train and make the thirty-minute troop down to the river in snake formation, stopping at every off-licence along the way and sending in their oldest members. It invariably rained, the river flooded our tent, we went twosies on cigarettes around campfires fuelled by toxic polystyrene chip containers, and drank our supplies. It was everything we hoped for.

But that year, I gave my friends the flick. I had an access-all-areas pass, thanks to my fanzine, and I didn't want them cramping my style. I took the train with a litre-bottle of cheap Scotch. No tent – I'd hustle and figure something out.

Backstage, I tried to attach myself to various groups. If I spotted someone I vaguely knew – a journalist or a PR – I'd muscle in on their cluster of plastic chairs, then keep reasonably quiet, particularly if it was my turn to buy a round.

After the festival had finished, I edged into the cab of some industry people and accompanied them to the hotel in town where everyone schmoozed. My cab-buddies disappeared as soon as we arrived, as people had a tendency to do when I wasn't looking, leaving me floating. The demographic in the hotel bar was disappointing. Where were the headline acts? Everyone was talking over everybody else's shoulders, watching the door.

I hung out with a couple of guys at the bar who toyed with me as to who they were. Were they locals? Were they band? Were they crew? Who did they know, for fuck's sake? They'd decided to be coy about it. One of them, a blond, accepted my offer of the dregs of my bottle of Scotch, and we covertly traded swigs when the bartender wasn't looking. And then I blacked out.

My memory was always patchy when I was drunk. I'd forget things I'd just said; where I'd been an hour earlier; the backstory of who I was speaking to; and increasing chunks of my vocabulary, which evaporated like bubbles in a bath. Sometimes I'd blackout for a whole hour; still talking rubbish, so who would even know? I'd had this problem since I was fourteen and accepted it as being as much a symptom of getting drunk as a hangover.

And so, when I came to, sprawled in some alleyway, watching the blond throw me one last look over his shoulder before hurrying out of sight, I didn't know what the finer details were. I just knew I'd been raped. It being 1993, I had no phone, no GPS. It took me a while, roaming around in distress, to discover that I was in a service alley down the side of the hotel.

In the lobby, I told the concierge I had been raped. I clung to the edge of his desk, expecting a flurry of efficient action, but the concierge and the receptionists just exchanged looks. Something was wrong here. The hotel shimmered goldenly in my peripheral vision. 'He was in your bar,' I urged, looking over my shoulder at the doorway. 'I can point him out.'

The concierge roused himself and walked me to the bar, where I hovered at the door, unwilling to cross the threshold. I scanned the crowd, but the blond and his mate were gone.

'Can you take me to the police station?' I asked the concierge. He returned to the lobby and began to wipe down the lounge tables with a cloth. Dumbly, I followed him from table to table. I searched for meaning in his deft strokes, my stockings balled up in my hand. The receptionists watched and whispered between themselves. *What sort of girl* ... I fancied them saying. My uniform at the time was fishnets, leather skirt, mesh top, black bra. If you weren't specifically into the oeuvre of the Chicago record label Wax Trax, you might not get all the references and just think it was a bit slutty.

When he was good and ready, the concierge took the lead out into the street, striding ahead like a peeved parent. The police station was only a few blocks away.

'She says she's been raped.' I saw the concierge raise his eyebrows at the desk sergeant in the universal language for 'we've got a right one here', before leaving. I blacked out again.

Then I was sitting in an interview room. I'd never been in a police station before. One detective, if that was his ranking, sat at the table with me. The other stood with his arms folded, leaning against the door. The look on his face suggested he'd given up on this already, while the nearest guy's face was arranged in disappointment. It seemed I'd had my medical examination. I'd given my statement. And now I'd changed my mind.

'Did you put your stockings back on?'

I looked down. They were ripped, but on my legs. 'I suppose so.'

Women weren't faring well in rape cases in 1993. As I sat at the table, my statement in front of me written out by someone else, I recalled the newspaper article about a prosecutor who clamped his hands together, then instructed the complainant to try to break his grip by inserting her hand. He weaved his arms about, supposedly representing her thrashing legs. 'You can't, can you?' he mocked her. So how could a man possibly have penetrated her with his rapey cock?

I could barely describe the bloke in the hotel bar, nor why we wound up where we did, nor the route I walked to this room. It must have been hours ago because they'd already collected CCTV footage of us leaving the hotel. 'I want to go home,' I said. Yes, I was sure.

A victim support officer drove me to Slough and made light conversation about my imminent start at university, until I got out like a shot at my parents' house. A few days later, she made a follow-up call. I got to the phone first.

'Please don't call here again,' I said, and hung up.

Actually, that's not the whole story. I remember one last thing before the blackout obliterated the rest, and it's something I'd put out of my mind until now, for my own wellbeing.

What kind of girl says to a stranger at a hotel bar, whom she has been plying with whisky, 'Do you want to go for a walk?'

It was one in the morning, probably. No time for a stroll.

Do you want to go for a walk?

The question was loaded with something alluring, something darkly mysterious. These were qualities I had been trying on like hats of late, testing my newfound power. I hadn't thought my question through to its logical conclusion; I didn't think anything through to its logical conclusion till I was nearly thirty.

Writing this chapter, though, I've got a few more questions. What kind of girl knowingly fails to pack a tent? What would her plan be? Then again, a girl who hasn't packed a tent certainly hadn't planned to be discarded in an alley, as that would still leave her with nowhere to stay. A sliver of someone's hotel-room floor would have been ideal. Also, a girl who has willingly had sex doesn't go straight from the scene to the police, does she?

I remember running these questions through a loop in the weeks following the perhaps-rape, before becoming so distressed I decided to pack them away. Now I dig them out again.

Did you suggest going out for a smoke?

No, you could smoke in bars then.

Did you go out to buy some smokes?

But surely the hotel sold them.

Did you ask him to walk you to the train station?

Possibly. Look, the timetable says trains run all night. At least, they do now, two decades on.

But then, that's not what you said, is it?

In the weeks following that festival, I paced around my childhood bedroom, curtains drawn, something obliteratingly loud on the stereo. I replayed what I could in my mind, dropped the needle, replayed, dropped the needle, replayed. I desperately needed to know my precise involvement. I'd have given anything for graphic certainty or a verdict from above, but the blackout had fallen like the final curtain before the man and I had even reached the hotel's revolving doors, overlapped only briefly by the CCTV camera as we pushed through them.

Whether it was rape or not, I wasn't about to broadcast what happened in my summer holidays. It wasn't just self-doubt. I tried to imagine telling someone, but would stall on 'rape', even in my head. The shame of the word was immense. (A few years on I'd allow that I'd 'managed to get myself raped'.) I'd change the direction of my pacing, shake it off. And there was the stupid inevitability of it all. How could I confide in my mother when she'd foreseen this sort of thing?

According to the Australian Bureau of Statistics' one-off Women's Safety Survey in 1996, only eighteen per cent of women who had experienced physical or sexual assault in the previous twelve months sought professional help. That low figure is near identical to one in the 2014 survey of seventy-six survivors of sexual violence, conducted by AVA (Against Violence and Abuse) in London. Then, nineteen per cent of survivors reported their experience to the police. Among those who did so, fifty-four per cent had a negative experience. A second survey by AVA was aimed at practitioners working with survivors of sexual violence. Thirty-seven per cent of these professionals claimed that they felt a sexual assault where the survivor was intentionally intoxicated would be taken much less seriously by police, and forty-four per cent believed a conviction would be much less likely. Incidentally, these results were published in a report provocatively titled *Not Worth Reporting*.

So that's sexual violence. Now imagine how few women would seek psychological help for something traumatic that fell into the 'grey area', that consensual twilight zone almost all women will stumble into at some point. I certainly felt that I couldn't waste a professional's time with anything less than the sort of violent ordeal that made front pages, just as I was sure sexual abuse didn't count unless it was incest. Instead, I just cried all the time. On trains. At gigs. Walking down the street.

A few months after the festival I left home and started university. In the first week I scanned the boards of the faculty staff and kept finding myself stopping in front of one photograph of a female academic in her fifties. She looked no-nonsense, but nice. Perhaps I could tell her.

And then the story ran in the Sunday newspaper, the one the *NME* journalist had written, about me and my fanzine. What was the fanzine called again? Oh yeah, *Slapper*. Northern slang for a promiscuous woman. You might remember the newspaper headline from a previous chapter: *More sex, please, we're groupies – and proud of it!*

That marked the end of the plan to tell. With this article

came confirmation, in black and white, that I was *that* kind of girl. The opportunist in the hotel bar, and his mate, would see it. He was off the hook. The academic would see it. My new flatmates and my tutors at university certainly had. I was forced to turn it all into a big joke. I never wrote another issue of *Slapper*. I dyed my hair a no-room-for-misunderstandings black and shut up.

Another cause of blackout is drink spiking. But, say the experts I talk to, spiking is rarely the result of a 'date-rape drug' being poured into a drink. It's more complicated than that.

In 2003, the first comprehensive study of drink spiking in Australia was published by the Chemistry Centre in Western Australia. It reported that, of the forty-four cases analysed, no trace of sedatives was found. Four years later, another report presented the toxicology results of around 100 people presenting at two Perth hospitals as victims of spiking. Of those, there wasn't one case in which a sedative was likely to have been slipped into a drink. Twenty-eight per cent of individuals had illicit drugs in their system that they admitted to taking themselves.

Yes, I reasoned upon reading this, but a drug such as GHB, a nervous-system depressant nicknamed 'grievous bodily harm', leaves your system notoriously quickly – within twelve hours. And what about all the women who *don't* report being spiked? As 2004's National Project on Drink Spiking in Australia reports, 'It is estimated that less than fifteen per cent of suspected drink-spiking sexual assaults are reported to police.'

Okay, so it's not that spiking doesn't happen. It's just that the bogeyman in a bar with a bottle of GHB in his back pocket is rare – the perpetrator has to get their victim out of there for a start. Instead, incapacitation is usually achieved with extra shots of alcohol, like when that gent in your group gets you a drink and comes back with a triple vodka masquerading as a single. And just as rape is far more likely to occur in a domestic setting by a person who is familiar, spiking is usually carried out back at someone's house, maybe after the clubs have closed. Maybe you're given a line of ketamine instead of coke, or someone prepares you a fix with a strength you weren't expecting. It's still spiking.

Dr Paul Quigley is an emergency medicine specialist and clinical toxicologist at Wellington Regional Hospital. He says, 'Of all of the cases where I have been to court giving evidence in confirmed cases of drug-facilitated sexual assault, the spiking occurred in a private venue. It often involves men who could have as many sexual partners as they want – that's not the issue. They've often made a relationship with the victim, and the victim was probably going to have consensual sex anyway, but the perpetrator enjoys complete dominance. They then take the most advantage out of the effects of the agents they use – the amnesia, loss of consciousness, doubt.'

But back to bars. What's more common an issue is 'prank spiking' with GHB or a similar agent. The perpetrator is more than likely somebody within your group who wants a joke at your expense, and they can watch you stumble around foolishly, without having to bundle you past security and into a cab. It's still just as dangerous; apart from potential death from overdose, I mean.

The victim is left vulnerable to predators and is liable to have their wallet or bag lifted by an opportunistic thief. Certainly, the police view it as assault.

Some pubs were quick to capitalise on this. As Paul Dillon, director of Drug and Alcohol Research and Training Australia (DARTA), tells me, pubs in Victoria in 2008 were printing coasters with the message *Your drink has been left unattended* and getting bar staff to leave them atop glasses. More often than not the returning woman would panic and buy another – a nice little earner for the hotel. Actually, the energy of these establishments would be better spent training their bar staff to look out for men ordering double and triple shots, then watching where those drinks are delivered.

There are also things that can mimic spiking, including drinking on medication (even a low-level antidepressant or sleeping agent); drinking fast, particularly on an empty stomach; or drinking early in the day. (If you jump to chapter nine, you'll also see at what point in her menstrual cycle a female is more affected by drink and drugs.)

GHB isn't available in shops anymore. In the early 1990s it was sold in health stores as a dietary supplement for bodybuilders, because a Japanese study found that if you took GHB and went to sleep you lost body fat and built muscle. It was also widely available in sex shops, bought to lower inhibitions in a similar way to amyl nitrate.

These days you're more likely to run into black-market batches of the industrial solvent GBL, consumed willingly by revellers in order to feel wasted, and also by ice users to come down. It's metabolised into GHB by the body, which can take longer, causing consumers – who don't know which version they've got – to sometimes assume a dose has not worked and top up dangerously. In April 2016, police seized $100,000 worth of GBL on the Gold Coast, which was being distributed at festivals in soy-sauce containers shaped as little fish. In February 2017, more than twenty festival-goers were hospitalised in Melbourne after overdosing on what was believed to be GHB.

What actually happens when you drink GHB or GBL? I can be your human guinea pig there. Semi-regularly I would buy a small bottle from a sex shop in Soho and drink it down the pub for a cheap high, which, if I were ranking things I've done in order of dangerousness, would actually be top of the list. It tasted salty, but certainly some drinks could disguise that. And besides, as Dillon says, 'since it's liquid, sometimes a person might willingly drink it, misunderstanding that it's a drug'.

If I got the dose wrong – by which I mean if I had already drunk a lot of alcohol or dropped a pinger – I would conk out. Upon coming to, I wouldn't realise I'd even been away, until I looked around the pub and noticed the demographic had changed. Additionally, my boyfriend would be shaking me in a rage, having been fending off the interest of bouncers for the past hour. On one occasion I was dimly aware of a flying sensation – as it turned out, being carried out of the pub – before coming to in a cab en route to home.

GHB/GBL leaves the system rapidly, which means a urine sample really needs to be given within about four hours if spiking is suspected. The problem is, substances used by predators include

Rohypnol, temazepam, Xanax, and the epilepsy medication clonazepam, and not every drug will be screened for by hospitals; in fact, I'm anecdotally told that one hospital will sometimes tell a patient they have found traces of a spiking drug in her system, purely to pacify her. Thankfully it's become easier to make a much more reliable, retroactive report through hair sampling. A person can register their complaint with the police then report back a month later to give a hair sample. In fact, most illicit drugs can also be tested for this way.

As for police, Quigley says they'll be looking for a secondary outcome: drug-facilitated robbery or assault. 'If you wake up in someone else's place and you have no idea of how you got there, yes, you should definitely look into that,' he says. 'Emergency departments aren't the place to do that – although a lot of the people we see in the emergency department, their level of intoxication is so high that they do need to be seen anyway and looked after. For reporting, you should go through a sexual-assault team, rape centres, or even direct to the police, because the testing that's required of blood and urine needs to be done at a forensic level.'

Paul Dillon is painfully aware of spiking being an emotive subject. After a quote in a women's magazine about spiking being a myth was wrongly attributed to him, he received death threats. 'Even if the evidence doesn't show that it happens as much as we think, it undoubtedly does happen,' he clarifies. 'And regardless of whether somebody has been spiked or not, they believe they have been and as a result they've gone through a major traumatic experience. To dismiss it would be completely inappropriate.'

I wish I had understood this, back when I was agonising over whether or not a crime had technically been committed in that alleyway. The trauma exists regardless, and without professional help it's likely to persist.

Back in 1993, the turd on the tube seat was an excellent find. Whoever had deposited it had since departed the London Underground, but they'd done me a massive favour. It was an act of public aggression, and I was claiming it.

By now, I lived in London, at one end of the Piccadilly Line. When I got on the tube the carriage would be reasonably empty, but with each stop it would fill up. Taking the seat opposite a freshly laid log would spare me the stress of human company. Sure enough, every commuter made a beeline for the free seat, recoiled, looked at me and retreated. Thank you, mysterious stranger.

I wasn't dealing well with this was-I-or-was-I-not-raped stuff. I'd stopped drinking for five weeks, seizing the incident as the chance to turn my life around. But I was eighteen. A life without alcohol would be no life at all. I started drinking again, and with that came a fatalistic acceptance: I knew my level of consumption made it impossible to stay safe, yet I had made my choice. I wouldn't be able to cry victim again, not even to myself.

Speed, I reasoned, ought to keep me from passing out and being unsafe, but somewhere along the way there had been a tipping point. The euphoric element had switched from making me feel empathetic and enigmatic to paranoid and grandiose.

Associate Professor Nicole Lee, from the National Drug

Research Institute, explains that at low doses stimulants – such as speed, meth and coke – enhance the mood. 'They increase dopamine, making you feel a lot more confident and focused. Your memory improves, and because of the increased serotonin, there's more optimism. If you're feeling vulnerable, stimulants will make you feel much more confident. If you've got mental health symptoms making your head a bit fuzzy, they'll improve that as well.'

But that's only at low doses. When people become dependent, they tend to use stimulants to ward off withdrawal symptoms, and the benefits they were seeking disappear. 'They experience more of the negative symptoms they were trying to get rid of,' Lee says. 'Paranoia and hyper-vigilance might increase, as would depression. For some people, their confidence could increase until they feel like superwoman, but in reality they're quite manic, with an element of being delusional.'

For me, London became a city of eight million adversaries. I prowled the platforms like Travis Bickle, lodging every *psst, psst*; every deliberate swerve into my path; every man who sat in the carriage with legs spread, moving his hand around by his crotch to draw a glance. My hyper-vigilance wasn't helped by the fact that I'd been in a fiery car crash earlier that year, with some random young drunks I'd met down the pub. The crashing of branches and crackling of flames invaded my dreams and, by day, I was alert for imminent disaster. I'd walk under scaffolding and picture it toppling down on top of me, or imagine a knife in my back, or being shoved under the tube. My paranoia became a persecution complex. Even the cars and hedgerows were looking at me funny.

So I was drawing attention to myself. What man wouldn't look twice at a weird girl vibrating with rage as we waited three minutes for the next train? I became combative, out-staring my adversaries, violently slamming my limbs around as I took a seat, alarming anyone lost in their own little world. Half the time I was deliberately seeking out soft targets: closing in on commuters simply minding their own business and lurking right behind them. Once in my seat, I ostentatiously read Valerie Solanas' *SCUM Manifesto*.

I'm not naturally that antisocial. My default setting is one of very British politeness; of waiting to get home to eat a cold pie, rather than eat a hot one on the train and risk causing my fellow passengers discomfort or envy; and of crossing to the other side of the street when walking behind someone at night, so as not to make them alarmed. But amphetamines and anger are a particularly toxic combination.

Right then, the tip of power in my favour felt good, and the bag of speed zipped into the sleeve of my bomber jacket became a weapon in my psychic warfare. Speeding off my tits served two purposes: I would look mad *and* unapproachable; and I might become bold enough to take a swing at someone, should the situation call for it. Anyway, I had bought a flick-knife in a dodgy shop in Hounslow and cradled it in the palm of one hand.

Feeling as though I was on the outskirts of society brought with it a sense of freedom. From now on, it was shoot first, ask questions later.

9

BODY OF EVIDENCE

The effects of substances on the female body and vice versa

Shortly before moving permanently to Australia in 2006, I went up into my parents' attic and pulled down the plastic bag of old diaries from my twenties. Each one had been bound in gaffer tape, the seal of which bore my signature.

In my childhood bedroom, I sliced through the tape of the first diary and methodically ripped out every page. I fed each one into my father's paper shredder.

If there was any danger of me deciphering the odd sentence – unlikely with my handwriting further messed up by amphetamines – I squinted until it was safely confetti. An hour later there was a metre-high heap of stringy paper that I wrestled down to the compost heap.

'I'll never want to revisit my old life,' I thought confidently.

But I still have my medical records. The substance-related entries begin when I was twenty-one.

26 June 1996: Tonsillectomy postponed after admission of heroin use the night before.

27 February 1997: Hyperventilation, numbness, anxiety, depersonalisation. Started after being fired from job. Long chat: teach breathing.

7 March 1997: As above.

19 March 1997: As above.

26 March 1997: As above. Asked about substance use. Regular amphetamine user 4 × week since teenager. Alcohol 35 units p/w.

12 April 1997: Panic attacks since yesterday. Took amphetamine yesterday. Can't cope without. Referred to Hampstead Road Centre for weekly appointments.

10 July 1997: Put on Prozac 20mg. Using alcohol and speed at present. Has returned to work.

9 October 1997: Stopped any amphetamine-like drugs. Stopped smoking. No panic attacks/paranoia. Discussed long-term effects of amphetamines. Wants to come off Prozac.

~Two-year breather for a supportive relationship~

24 February 2000: Complaining of tingling. Shallow breathing. Taking stimulants.

29 February 2000: Cuts and bruises not healing. Polydipsia [thirst]; episodes of paraesthesia [pins and needles] all over except trunk; anxiety.

7 March 2000: Paraesthesia and Raynaud's testing at Whittington Hospital. Inconclusive.

12 July 2000: Paroxysmal dysesthesia testing at National Hospital for Neurology and Neurosurgery. Two years ago she complained of a prickling in her legs. Has progressed into all extremities and is now painful. Since she stopped taking amphetamines it has decreased to twice a week.

1 November 2001: Effusion of right knee from a fall while drinking.

28 June 2005: Operation for squint after severing abducens nerve. [Head injury was acquired from a shopping-trolley ride on ketamine.]

My medical records exemplify the way in which women's drug use can be glossed over by GPs, meaning women tend not to enter treatment until they're more advanced in dependence than men. Throughout all of these appointments, I'm not exactly misdiagnosed – my sprained knee, wobbly eyeball and probable paraesthesia (which can stem from stimulant use, alcohol use and B12 deficiency – itself a side effect of alcohol use) do indeed need attending to. Yet the root cause of these ailments, the substance use, is ignored in all but one visit, at which point a referral to a specialist service is made. Actually, I was amazed not to find 'borderline personality disorder' – code for 'time waster' – scrawled on my notes.

The term 'telescoping' is often applied to women who seek treatment. It describes the seemingly accelerated progression that women have over men, from first trying a substance to becoming dependent on it, to suffering greater withdrawal. According to one 2004 study of men and women abusing cannabis, opioids and alcohol, women's use escalates quicker than men's, and women report more severe psychiatric, medical and employment complications. They also find it harder to quit.

However, Dr Nadine Ezard of St Vincent's Hospital believes this to be a fallacy. There's a middle ground of women with low-to-moderate dependence whose stats are rarely included because either they do not come forward for treatment (perhaps they have childcare issues), or are not put forward by GPs for treatment. It's also not uncommon for women presenting with substance-use issues – as I did – to be diagnosed solely as having anxiety or depression, and to be sent away with a course of antidepressants.

'There develops this idea of "telescoping", but I don't buy it. It's just that women are much more invisible until the last moment,' says Ezard.

Females who drink heavily are also prone to other serious conditions – such as high-blood pressure, cirrhosis, nerve damage (alcoholic polyneuropathy or peripheral neuropathy), weakening of the heart muscle and damage to the brain – in a much shorter timeframe of drinking than males.

Short-term – or even one-off – drug use is also riskier for females. In 1995, two teenage girls in two different hemispheres died of water intoxication and hyponatremia – low sodium in the blood. Leah Betts in the UK, and Anna Wood in Australia, had both taken ecstasy (as previously mentioned in chapter five), then had drunk litres of water – possibly because drug agencies at the time warned of the dangers of getting dehydrated while dancing. This over-hydration diluted the levels of sodium in their blood, which caused convulsing, coma and death.

High-profile publicity campaigns from the parents of both girls have helped warn other consumers of the risks of both ecstasy and over-hydrating, but what's not as commonly known is that females are more at risk generally. A study from the Netherlands looked at the high incidence of mild hyponatremia in females using ecstasy at a 2010 rave party in Amsterdam called Awakenings. Their sixty-three subjects – male and female – were identified as having taken MDMA by a urine test. Their plasma sodium concentration was then tested.

The researchers found that only three per cent of the males developed mild hyponatremia during the event, as opposed to twenty-five per cent of the females. It's not just down to the fact that women were taking more care to stay hydrated and then misjudging the safe amount. MDMA increases plasma copeptin in females, but not males, and so females report more thirst and the sensation of a dry mouth after taking the drug. The plasma sodium concentration is also slightly lower in females in the luteal phase of their menstrual cycle.

Hyponatremia, incidentally, can also be induced by long-distance running. Again, this occurs more frequently in females.

Many academics and psychologists, including leading personality and motivational psychologist David McClelland, have theorised over the years that men with a power motive are drawn to alcohol, and that it becomes an emblem of their superiority, since traditionally it has largely excluded women. It's an idea I explored in chapter two when examining my own internal misogyny.

For women, the most emblematic substance seems to be nicotine. The rate of young female smokers is rising as the rate of young male smokers falls. That's the finding of a 2014 bulletin from the UK's Office for National Statistics. I began smoking at thirteen to appear older and more sophisticated, which is generally a goal for girls at a younger age than boys. Women and girls often also use cigarettes as a diet aid, which many drug and alcohol workers observe when their female clients give up ice and are dismayed by the resulting weight gain. Smoking may also be seen as a more acceptable crutch than drugs and alcohol by some women, particularly older women.

More broadly, people often smoke to 'calm the nerves'. Perhaps it's really more of a welcome distraction than a balm, because nicotine is actually an anxiogenic, meaning it increases anxiety. Cigarettes are also handy in times of social anxiety; in fact, smoking is the reason I avoid soirees in which people will be drinking.

I'm not worried I'll drink; I just know I can't sit still for more than ten minutes in company without some kind of prop. Unfortunately, the effects of nicotine-exacerbated anxiety might be long-lasting. Research from Columbia University in 2000 revealed that people who smoked heavily as teenagers were seven times more likely to suffer generalised anxiety disorder in early adulthood.

Then there's the relationship between nicotine and stimulants: one cross-potentiates the other, as studies with rats have found, which means they make each other more effective. And as anyone who 'can only smoke when I'm drinking' will attest, nicotine and alcohol go together pleasingly – because both target the mesolimbic dopamine system, and cross-tolerance between the two may reduce the drugs' aversive effects.

Lastly, it may surprise you to learn that smoking is the biggest killer of people who have quit substances. This is because the individual continues or increases smoking (or, in my case, starts smoking again), partly in an effort to release the dopamine spikes they had grown accustomed to from their substance use, and partly because of the cigarette's ability to be both a distraction and a social tool.

Hugely underestimated by the laywoman is the role that her hormones play in substance use. A female's menstrual cycle causes fluctuations in her renal, cardiovascular, haematological, and immune systems, so it makes sense that these fluctuations would have a knock-on effect on the way her body processes substances. For a heavy imbiber, any such fluctuations in intoxication are likely to go unnoticed amid the general chaos of artificial highs and plummeting lows, but with a few pointers (and a period-tracker app) they can be observed and perhaps even worked around.

WEEK ONE: THE MENSTRUAL PHASE During a female's period, the fatigue and low resilience of heavy-flow days are likely to hasten the effects of drugs and alcohol. In short, if you were ever likely to conk out at the bar by nine, odds are it would be in week one of the cycle. Due to low levels of estrogen and testosterone, things also hurt more. That includes hangovers.

WEEK TWO: THE FOLLICULAR PHASE The glorious run-up to ovulation, in which estrogen levels are rising and in which nothing can possibly go wrong. Actually, people are just as prone to benders and relapses during high times as well as lows. I tend to smoke more around ovulation – the same time I can barely keep my hands off myself. Females are more responsive to stimulants in this follicular phase. Estrogen is thought to sensitise the brain to THC – the psychoactive component of cannabis. Studies also suggest that high levels of estrogen equate to impulsive behaviour.

WEEK THREE: THE OVULATORY PHASE The fun police – that's progesterone – arrive. There's evidence that estrogen and progesterone act as a yin and yang when it comes to our interaction with drugs, with estrogen making substances more attractive and progesterone tempering the urges. When rats are given supplemental estrogen, they accept an offer of cocaine more quickly than rats without estrogen. But if the rats are also given supplemental progesterone, the interest in cocaine is tempered. (If, like me, you have estrogen dominance, commit this information to heart and use 'hormonal imbalance' as your new favourite excuse.)

WEEK FOUR: THE LUTEAL PHASE Estrogen and testosterone both plunge. The stereotype of the premenstrual female is of her face-planting a bar of chocolate. Less frequently reported on, but equally rewarding, are alcohol, cigarettes and drugs – alcohol additionally because women with PMS crave carbohydrates.

Other than causing interesting interactions throughout the monthly cycle, what else happens when substances and sex hormones combine? Well, estrogen doesn't only make substances more attractive; some studies suggest it slows down their elimination. This means estrogen-based birth-control pills might extend the effects of intoxication from drugs and alcohol.

Alcohol also raises estrogen levels, and higher estrogen levels can worsen symptoms of polycystic ovary syndrome, fibroids and endometriosis, as well as increase the risk of breast cancer. In 2009 the *Journal of the National Cancer Institute* published the findings of researchers that for every ten grams of alcohol consumed per day – which is one standard drink – there was an eleven per cent increase in the risk of developing breast cancer.

Trans women receiving doses of estrogen will also find that substances affect them differently. There's a gap in the research, says Dr Nadine Ezard, when it comes to the interactions and cross-interactions of hormone replacement therapy (HRT) and recreational drug use, or even substitute drug use. Methadone, for example, is known to cause a hormone imbalance, but just how that would affect somebody on HRT is as yet unclear. According to TouchBase, an online resource for LGBTQI Australians, cyproterone acetate, which is often prescribed to intersex people and trans women, reacts poorly to large quantities of alcohol. After a night on the turps, those who use the medication can feel particularly lethargic and unable to concentrate. Prolonged use in dosages upwards of 150 milligrams can lead to liver damage – which, of course, isn't helped by heavy drinking.

By contrast, HRT in perimenopausal and menopausal females can help prevent the 'progesterone drop-out' that can cause anxiety and depression, which in turn increases the likelihood of self-medication. In particular, females suffering low progesterone might be attracted to alcohol and benzodiazepines such as Xanax, because these substances can quell anxiety.

Professor Jayashri Kulkarni from the Monash Alfred Psychiatry Research Centre tells me that estrogen plays a protective role in the brain as an antipsychotic and an antidepressant. If that is compromised – which can happen in a person who has experienced early-life trauma – 'you get this chronic premenstrual exacerbation of depression, but what's really bad is the perimenopause around the mid-forties. Women really start to deteriorate again and some of the stuff of their early life comes back to hit them again.'

There a few things that incur judgement like the sight of a pregnant woman with a drink in her hand, yet according to the National Drug Strategy Household Survey of 2013, one in four women continue to drink once they know they're pregnant – and that's probably a conservative estimate.

You could be forgiven for not knowing what the safe limit of alcohol consumption is for a pregnant woman, given the wealth of conflicting information from GPs, public health campaigns, magazines and maternity literature. Societal norms are prone to fluctuations over the years; and there's certainly no international consensus. Actually, the message from Australia's National Health and Medical Research Council is that 'not drinking is the safest option' but, as recently as 2006, national clinical guidelines were released that cautiously allowed seven standard drinks a week and no more than two a day. These guidelines even advised that 'an abstinence-based approach is not recommended, in part because it could result in precipitous anxiety'.

It's a sticky topic. Writing for *The Drum* in 2014, feminist commentator Clementine Ford envisages a future in which women are forced into the position of 'glorified broodmare'. She's responding to the news of a council in the UK pursuing criminal-injuries compensation for a six-week-old baby born with fetal alcohol syndrome (FAS).

'The bodies of women – and the bodies of pregnant women especially – have always been heavily legislated, both by political governance and social mores,' Ford writes. 'Fetal personhood laws pose a danger to women the world over, because they remove the right to choice and autonomy from those people whose bodies are given over to the development of a fetus.'

An additional point that highlights this slippery slope: if we're going to body-police women in case they harm their unborn children, couldn't that extend to mean that any woman of child-bearing age shouldn't be able to drink at all – just in case she's unwittingly pregnant?

What's unanimous is that the first trimester is thought to be the riskiest. Of course, this is the period in which a woman can be unaware that she is pregnant, and the Australian Medical Association calculates that one in three women will drink through it. In her book *Out of Time*, British journalist Miranda Sawyer recounts finding out she was pregnant after a bout of heavy drinking, at which point she fretted at the thought of her fetus twirling about in vodka. But, she writes, an irony also became apparent: 'Friends said, "Oh, how would anyone get pregnant without booze?"'

No woman wants to harm her unborn child, but 'harm' remains an unknown quantity. A 2012 study by researchers at the North Dakota Fetal Alcohol Syndrome Center found that alcohol elimination from the fetus relies on the mother's metabolic capacity. This can vary eightfold among pregnant women, which might at least partially explain why some women can drink moderately throughout pregnancy without any discernible effects on the child and others simply cannot.

Being hungover, or even high, reduces the ability to read the nuances of the body, and can mask early signs of pregnancy, such as nausea and fatigue. Teratogens – such as cocaine, methamphetamine and, again, alcohol – are drugs that can cause birth defects, as well as premature birth, miscarriage, and placental deficiency or abruption, and can cause a baby to be born with withdrawal symptoms.

The spectrum of potential harms can be caused by alcohol consumption at any point throughout the pregnancy, but fetal alcohol syndrome (FAS) is the most severe form of fetal alcohol spectrum disorder (FASD), and is derived from damage done in the gastrulation period, in the third week after conception.

Dr Janet Hammill is the coordinator of the Collaboration for Alcohol Related Development Disorders (CARDD) at the University of Queensland. For decades she's been an advocate for children and adults who have been invisible to early diagnosis and intervention. She says, 'Babies exposed to alcohol before birth have a higher incidence of smaller or misshapen kidneys, which means there is not the capacity in those kidneys to do what they're meant to do. So that baby will develop kidney disease earlier, and if they begin drinking – because they're born addicted to alcohol – they face significant problems.'

As well as potential damage to the organs and central nervous system, there can be growth deficiency and facial anomalies, such as a smooth philtrum – the groove above the upper lip; small, close-set eyes with epicanthal folds in the inner corners; a thin upper lip; a flat nasal bridge; and a double crease in the outer ears.

'If it's not diagnosed early, the primary disabilities then become secondary,' Hammill cautions, describing a litany of behavioural problems. 'The worst of it is the arson, running away, cruelty to animals, early school dropout, mental health problems, inappropriate sexual behaviour, self-harming and suicide. Suicide is an enormous concern. The life expectancy of someone with fetal alcohol syndrome is thirty-four, and I think the high rates of suicide influence that.'

Perhaps the biggest problem is that FASD is self-perpetuating because of the impulsive, risk-taking behaviour it facilitates. 'It's very much trans-generational,' says Hammill. 'People who have it can't control their fertility. They can't be relied on to take the pill.' They're also more likely to drink or take drugs during their own pregnancy.

It's difficult to estimate how many children are born with FASD in Australia each year. Dr Doug Shelton, a child specialist who runs a FASD clinic on the Gold Coast, told the ABC's *Four Corners* program that up to one million Australians could be on the spectrum. He also thinks the myth needs to be busted that FASD is an Indigenous problem. It's true that remote Aboriginal communities are considered to be high risk but, as Elizabeth Elliott, Professor of Paediatrics and Child Health at the University of Sydney, writes for *The Conversation* in 2016, it's also problematic that most of the research has been limited to those areas. 'We don't really know the scale of the problem in other parts of Australia, because no other population-based prevalence data are available anywhere in the nation,' she notes.

According to Katrina Chamberlain, a provisional psychologist at Griffith University and Wesley Mission who gave a talk at the Gold Coast's Addiction 16 conference about the diagnostic process for children with prenatal alcohol exposure, the figure is likely to be higher than the rates of autism, cerebral palsy, spina bifida and SIDS combined.

'The education system needs to catch up, and many health professionals need to be educated themselves,' she says. 'The child is often mistaken for being bad or naughty. Often these children are misdiagnosed with other disorders – one of those being ADHD – due to their executive-function deficits, such as impulsivity, and inability to plan, organise and follow instructions.'

Chamberlain is of the opinion that Australia is lagging behind on global discussions about FASD. 'People working in the field tend to say it's a disability but it's not officially,' she tells me. 'If you were tested and had an IQ under seventy, you could qualify as having an intellectual disability.'

As of 2016 a diagnostic tool has started to be rolled out, created by the Australian FASD Collaboration. In the meantime, case workers continue to make their own deductions about clients, based on family history, but the diagnosis process is complex, requiring multi-disciplinary teams of allied health professionals. It's arduous for the child – if the child's behaviour is even picked up on at all.

And that's alcohol. What of other drugs? Consumption of substances affects both men's and women's fertility by altering levels of hormones. In the case of women, cannabis can decrease levels of the luteinising hormone, while stimulants increase levels of prolactin. The effects of drug use during pregnancy itself are varied, but to focus on a growing problem, 'ice babies' can suffer all manner of birth defects, from cardiac problems to brain haemorrhage, cleft palate, delayed motor development, limb defects, hearing and vision defects, and memory and attention-span problems.

The onus shouldn't all be on expectant mothers anyway. There's evidence that men's own alcohol and drug consumption can affect a fetus at the point of fertilisation. A 2013 Korean study examined the trans-generational effects of paternal alcohol exposure in mouse offspring. Male mice exposed to alcohol went on to conceive fetuses with abnormal organ and/or brain development, as opposed to the normally developed fetus sired by those mice that were not exposed.

Additionally, Dr Janet Hammill cannot emphasise enough that fetal programming is not just affected by drug and alcohol exposure, but also by maternal stress, which elevates the levels of cortisol and can alter the development of the fetal brain. Such stress can arise from a disruptive home environment, or from a lack of support from a partner – particularly if the partner continues to use substances themselves.

It's when the kids move out that alcohol and drugs can quite unexpectedly move in. Baby boomers are experiencing the largest increase in illicit drug use and also the highest rate of daily drinking, according to reports by the National Drug Strategy and NSW Health.

There's a triple threat for women of that generation. Firstly, their children may recently have left home, which can instil a sense of purposelessness or loss, and may also shine a light on any problems within a marriage that have been glossed over. In a 2015 UK survey by YouGov, twenty-eight per cent of women over forty-five claimed to drink as much as, or more than, their adult kids. Secondly, if they're retired, or have been inched out of their jobs, there may be a corresponding loss of identity and usefulness. Thirdly, their hormonal imbalance yet again sets out to kneecap them, this time in the form of perimenopause or menopause, which can often be misdiagnosed as depression, since the symptoms vary so wildly from female to female. Menopause can bring with it the sort of identity crisis that puberty ushered in.

As we get older our bodies also metabolise substances less efficiently. The liver and stomach shrink to a smaller size and, as there's also less body fluid, there will be a more potent concentration of substances. On top of that, medical conditions such as high blood pressure, diabetes and high cholesterol make it harder to recover from the effects of drugs and alcohol.

While counsellors certainly see plenty of baby boomers with illicit drug problems, according to Australia's Annual Overdose Report by the Penington Institute in 2016, the number of prescription-drug overdoses by people in their fifties and sixties has tripled over ten years. It's likely that GPs are far less watchful about drug misuse with older patients and more inclined to allow repeat prescriptions; but, in any case, signs of intoxication can be mistaken for symptoms of old age. The most common culprits are benzodiazepines such as Valium, Xanax and temazepam; or opioid analgesics (painkillers), such as oxycodone, codeine, fentanyl and tramadol. Most of these can react negatively with alcohol, but even alone they can make an older person more prone to stumbles and falls.

Half the challenge is just admitting the problem, which isn't easy for an older generation that attaches more stigma to substance use. When I met the senior counsellors at Holyoake, which provides drug and alcohol services in Perth, they had high praise for older women who sought their help.

'It's another opportunity to address issues that weren't addressed in adolescence,' one counsellor reflects. 'There are seasons of life for a woman: puberty; settling down; maybe having a baby, at which point her self-esteem may drop because she's awake all night. There may be a separation, or she's starting to look older; the kids are going to school. These transitions can make us want to lean back into the past and use coping strategies such as drugs and alcohol. If there's no sense of purpose in life, you start dying inside.'

The beauty of periods of intense change, she says, is that they can be harnessed. 'These transitions can create opportunities for us to grow and reinvent ourselves. When women know there are things they can do to take responsibility for their own health, it can be incredible where that can then take them.'

10

YOUR BRAIN AS A POKIE MACHINE

Other risky behaviours that hit the dopamine jackpot

This chapter could equally have been called 'Actually, doctor, there *is* something else ...' Since one angle on addiction is that it's merely a symptom of psychological malaise, someone dependent on substances is likely to have other symptoms of that malaise. The most common symptomatic bedfellows are pathological gambling, compulsive sexual behaviour, compulsive internet use, compulsive buying and kleptomania, all of which are colloquially referred to as addictions.

'Been Caught Stealing' was Jane's Addiction's biggest hit, and quite the anthem in 1990. In his jerky bray, Perry Farrell describes his girlfriend stuffing supermarket loot down her skirt with gleeful entitlement. Coincidentally, 1990 was when my own stealing career began.

There's a certain newsagent at London's Paddington Station – it's changed its configuration now – that back then you could stroll in one door of and exit out another half a kilo heavier, as if you were just passing through. I'd want to buy the *NME* and a

Mars bar, but funds were tight if I were also to afford my four-pack of Gold Label Very Strong Special Beer (that's actually what it's called). This conundrum coincided with the new presence of a loud voice in my head that said, 'I want to do something *bad*.' Okay, nicking stuff from WHSmith was hardly a criminal masterplan, but having been in a fug of despondency I suddenly felt like I had purpose.

When I moved out of home, things escalated. I stole food from the share-house fridge; packs of cigarettes from pub tables; clothes from shops; jewellery from market stalls; people's boyfriends. When I got caught – which was almost always – I felt shame, but it was mixed in with anger, that people couldn't see past the stealing to the turmoil beyond it. I was just misunderstood.

It was a mystery to me why morals didn't come naturally. They'd been drilled into me, all right, but they didn't kick in automatically at the correct age of development. I learned via the most circuitous route that nobody likes a thief. And public humiliation was fortunately the silver bullet I needed to kill off the desire.

As Pulp's Jarvis Cocker warned in 'Common People' – in which a middle-class girl seeks the novelty of working-class life – nobody likes a tourist. But having just left home I launched myself into a North London community of squatters with anthropological zeal. As a young teenager I'd loved Penelope Spheeris' 1984 film *Suburbia* about a group of punk outcasts. Now I'd infiltrated such a group. My handler was called Fiona.

I'd met Fiona through the *NME* penpal ads. She had bleached dreads with shaved sides, and wore furry day-glo shorts with tons of hoops up her ears ... exactly like me. Her room in a dingy council flat was cheered up with bright appliques of 1960s-style flowers. The drug-taking was cheerful, too. If we were going out to a rave she'd make us both a berry-flavoured squash and then shake some speed into it, a nice little ritual in front of the telly. I'd swirl the squash around the glass to pick up all the fine powder. Even with the artificial berries working overtime, we'd have to try hard not to gag.

Speed was the drug of choice among the squatters, since it was only five quid a gram and was dealt prolifically among our number. I say 'our' number, but I believe I was the only person whose father was paying their rent and a weekly allowance as they studied at university.

Unlike the raggle-taggle urchins of *Suburbia* who stole from supermarkets, lived fast and died young, this crew was made up of seasoned employment-dodgers in their thirties who had been teenagers when punk hit in the mid-1970s. The music of choice by then, which I couldn't abide, was some really filthy techno: kind of punk, mark II. I'd find myself trailing Fiona and the others to illegal warehouse raves in Dalston, purely because that was where the drugs were going. Pills didn't make me want to dance or have sex; they just made me want to smoke. I'd stand there, puffing on the sidelines of some industrial tomb bisected by jittery green lasers. I wished they'd go to a nice cosy pub; somewhere with proper working toilets. Here, the toilet was a car park, where girls with lollipops in their mouths and pigtails stuck perpendicularly on their heads waited their turn to piss behind a van, at which point their traitorous kidneys would leave them hanging in a fruitless squat.

I scribbled notes on my fag packet, listening to the music build up to some horrible, squelching crescendo that seemed to get everybody excited. The smells come back to me now. Benson & Hedges, stale Red Stripe breath, wet German shepherds and smoke machines. I wore Body Shop white musk to mask it all and smoked my nice, clean, white menthols.

Despite these tiresome social commitments, being accepted into a group was a novelty. The reason I had spent my teenage years getting shitfaced alone was because nobody I knew would have wanted to commit to getting shitfaced to the same extent. Sometimes, in Squatopia, there was the genuine sense of community I yearned for, such as when we'd walk in a gang across the park to drink in a huddle, or indulge in the full English breakfasts at a shit cafe, or engage in cocaine parlour games, in which two girls would start at either end of a monster line that stretched across the whole table.

Over time Fiona increasingly adopted a hectoring tone with me because, she said, I would benefit from the wisdom of her five-year advantage in age. In fact, her irritation came from bringing someone into the group who flaunted all etiquette. Most concerning was my habit of turning up empty-handed to squats and parties. This sense of entitlement accounted for the cruel taunts of 'middle-class blagger' that Fiona assured me were being bandied around behind my back – although, if half of my detractors weren't secretly middle-class themselves, I'll eat Mum and Dad's National Trust membership card.

Women have little currency in drug-based scenes, and I was cheapening my value by the day. Being unskilled in conversation,

I found sex to be the most efficient way of acclimatising with a group, but by sleeping around I kept blundering into the ancient ruins of other people's relationships, and it seemed they were heritage-protected. My default was Turbo, a wiry Welshman with home tattoos (was that an Ace of Spades or a swastika?) and close-cropped black hair. Fiona's cock-blocker mode would be activated whenever Turbo lazily reached for my thigh in the pub. She'd swat him away with a clipped Scottish barb but, like a blowfly, he'd buzz back in a few seconds and alight on my leg.

Even though any tight scene is likely to have an incestuous history that involves its members in every conceivable sexual combination, I was the newest object of irritation. My most notable nemesis was Yvonne, a fierce-looking girl who didn't like the cut of my jib, nor where I left it. In group settings she was prickly, but I recognised the way she'd zero in on the one man drunker than the rest and smoothly low-talk him, making him her co-conspirator, angling herself into him. She'd eye the rest of us with a half-smirk from her corner there, her gang of two.

I couldn't figure out why the group accepted with resignation that Yvonne would sleep with everyone's boyfriend and leave scratches down his back for good measure. She was like the scheming man-eater on a Mexican soap opera. Were we that bored, sitting in the pub all day, that we needed a villain for entertainment? Still, I made her my yardstick for my own reputation. I did the equations of my promiscuity in my head and estimated I had a good few couplings in me before reaching the grand total of Yvonne.

A social soiree in Squatopia was usually a long haul at the pub, sat smoking by the dartboard, with Turbo putting the

Velvets on the jukebox for the eighth time. Being only fair-weather friends, we weren't inclined to learn each other's personal history; so to while away the hours we might snort ketamine. This messed with your sense of perception so that you staggered to and from the bar, which one minute was an inch away, the next many miles – to much hilarity.

As my morals eroded with the inhaled lines, I'd idly let my hand fall into the coat pocket of whichever dealer sat next to me. I'd feel around with my fingers then withdraw, a couple of pills or a rolled note secreted in my palm and a smirk of triumph on my face. These people were loaded in every sense of the word, I reasoned. How would they even notice?

The jig was up when I stole thirty pounds from the table of a coke dealer after crashing there for the night. I didn't even remember doing it till he found the loot in my boot. Still, I countered the rumour that was circulating by confronting the dealer at the pool table a week later and barefaced denied it.

'Who was it then?' Kev spat. 'Badger? My best mate of twenty years?'

'Maybe.' I shrugged, starting to believe it myself. Badger was indeed there that night, the furry little bastard. It was totally feasible.

But Kev wasn't even bothered about recrimination. His disgust was such that he simply continued with his game.

My days in this supposed den of iniquity were numbered. I had been attracted to the scene because any kind of behaviour would fly – or so I thought. I'd failed to recognise the importance of hierarchy and loyalty, or the fact that every community must have its scapegoat. For this role I had volunteered myself, and I sank to the bottom of the pile.

Even Yvonne was tolerated better than me now; but anyway, I had misjudged that dynamic. This group had known each other for decades and the status quo was well established. Yvonne stopped her nightly crying in the corner of the pub to crow in my direction, always surrounded by a gaggle of newfound supporters. Perhaps I shouldn't begrudge her that, but Turbo, who had been on the receiving end of many enthusiastic blow jobs, was another matter. He invited me around for a cider, then ambushed me with a group of girls, who lay on the couches like Caligulas guzzling grapes, and tore strips off me. Only halfway through my first can, I got up and left, to lurch sobbing down the street.

Theft within a tight-knit community is social suicide, but my chronic lack of self-respect made that quite appealing. I'd blub myself to sleep under an eiderdown of shame, wondering, 'How did this happen again?' – even as I listed all the ways. For now, my anthropological study of Squatopia was over, and I reluctantly returned my focus to my actual arts degree.

What was all that about, I wondered twenty years later? Why ostracise yourself for the sake of a few quid?

Calling my behaviour kleptomania might be a dramatic interpretation, but this does affect mostly women, with the female-to-male ratio estimated at three to one. It's classified as an impulse-control disorder, characterised by the inability to resist the impulse to steal, even when the objects are not needed.

A 2007 study found that more than ten per cent of its kleptomaniac subjects also had borderline personality disorder, which as I've described in chapter seven is thought of as a set of responses to childhood trauma, most commonly observed in women.

There are a few convincing schools of thought about why people steal. One is that stealing is a symptom of depression: theft counteracts low serotonin levels with a stimulating high. Another is that stealing compensates for real or threatened loss: some people engage in thieving jags that seem to rise up out of nowhere, but which are actually triggered by the loss of a job, the death of a loved one, or some other trauma. Another is that stealing is linked to obsessive-compulsive disorder, working as a distraction from intrusive thoughts.

Now on to the neuroscientific explanation. Stealing releases dopamine, in the same way that drug and alcohol use does. It was once thought that this chemical was released through pleasurable activity, to the point that it was wrongly nicknamed the 'feel-good chemical'. Now scientists hypothesise that it's released in a flood every time a reward is anticipated, rather than by the reward itself. Its evolutionary purpose is to motivate you towards goals necessary for survival, such as feeding yourself and procreating, but it's also being released when you walk into a clothes shop and start salivating, or when you reach for your phone to check for Instagram likes, or when you rummage for your packet of smokes.

Dopamine is particularly partial to risky decisions, such as stealing, gambling, cheating, illicit drug-taking, throwing up dinner in a bathroom close by to your dining companions, or having some other kind of double life. And this is why members of one twelve-step fellowship, such as Alcoholics Anonymous, will often attend others: Gamblers Anonymous, Debtors Anonymous, Sex and Love Addicts Anonymous. They're all basically Dopamine Anonymous. In fact, so closely are they linked that many pharmacological and psychological treatments can be used for multiple addictions.

Dopamine also digs unpredictability, so pokie machines, being a game of chance, are basically chemical factories, sometimes described as the hypodermic needle of gambling. Given what we now know about dopamine being triggered by anticipation, we can deduce gambling is not primarily motivated by winning money; it's about the chemical reward the brain gets by taking a risk. In 2010, researchers in Denmark measured dopamine release in a group of gamblers – and also in a control group. Both groups had equal releases of dopamine when experiencing a win, but the gamblers alone had pronounced dopamine release even when experiencing a loss.

That's something game-makers have come to capitalise on with their algorithms. Dr Adrian Carter, a senior research fellow at Monash University's Brain and Mental Health Laboratory, says, 'Gamblers will actually get a bigger kick out of a near miss than they do for a win, so there's a particular design feature that trades on this response – it's when the last spinning wheel appears that it is going to give a win, but then just turns over at the last second to a loss.'

There are rules for designers about the number of near misses that are allowed, although the regulations differ by jurisdiction.

Carter adds wryly, 'Pokie designers probably know more about the neuropsychology of gambling addiction than most scientists – they're better funded.'

This explains the desire of people with problematic gambling – or problematic substance use – to persevere when the odds are against them: they have an increased dopamine susceptibility towards certain types of decisions. As it's often ruefully noted in recovery groups for gambling and substance use alike: 'Insanity is doing the same thing over and over again, and expecting different results'. In some ways it's not so insane, when what you're chasing is the dopamine hit and you'll get it regardless of whether you win or lose.

Compulsive buying is another related behaviour that – as you might imagine – has a gender bias towards women. Sometimes there's an underlying eating disorder; in fact, quite often when a woman shoplifts or indulges in a compulsive-spending spree, she'll return items a few days later, engaging in something resembling a binge-and-purge cycle.

It's become increasingly common to call compulsive internet use (CIU) an addiction – though, as Dr Carter tells me, that's a contested issue. 'The things that people tend to engage with on the internet compulsively – or repeatedly, to be more precise – tend to be activities that they might become addicted to in the real world, such as shopping, gambling, porn and gaming. Is it that the internet is addictive or just facilitates addictive activities?'

Broadly speaking, Gen Y is thought to abstain from substances more than previous generations; in the UK, according to a National Health Service survey, smoking and alcohol use is at its lowest among young people since such records began in 1982, and drug use among under-sixteens is down twenty-nine per cent from 2001. This might in part be attributed to bans on cigarette advertising, tighter regulation around alcohol consumption, and increased taxes, but perhaps this lack of interest can also be attributed to their reward activity being funnelled into social media activity.

Sex, of course, rewards us with dopamine since it's vital for our survival. In hypersexual individuals there's overactivity of the reward circuits, whether it be from the thrill of the chase, the challenge of getting another person to bend to your will, or explorations of the taboo. Those so persuaded fit the personality type described in chapter three: risk-taking sensation-seekers with rash impulsivity and a predilection for instant gratification. In times of stress or boredom, hypersexuality is likely to be heightened, just as substance use may increase. In an attempt to distract themselves from anxiety, some might slip into a period of perpetual sexual fantasy or infatuation until there's no room for anything else. Or they might take bigger and bigger risks. Hypersexuality prevalence is also high in people presenting with borderline personality disorder (as outlined in chapter seven); bipolar disorder; and ADHD (particularly the inattentive sub-type – now you know what they're *really* thinking about).

Would it surprise you to learn that shame itself is a real dopamine squirter? Along with pride and guilt, it activates the dorsomedial prefrontal cortex, amygdala, insula and the nucleus accumbens. No wonder there's the urge to wallow in it some-times; in fact, sex addicts might be dopamine double-dipping.

It's simplistic to just point the finger at dopamine, though. There are all kinds of brain chemicals at play here. Low serotonin, for instance, causes higher anxiety and depression, but also higher libido.

Just as a person builds up a tolerance to substances, so can they build up a tolerance to the dopamine release that other high-reward activities provide. It's a process called neuroadaptation. The brain compensates for all this stimulation by down-regulating the dopamine receptors. The remaining receptors also become desensitised to dopamine. Now the individual must double their efforts – and try ever-riskier manoeuvres – to feel any reward. We automatically think of a bigger hit of a drug, but apply the same principle to gambling: an individual might raise the stakes with larger amounts of money as the years go by. Or apply it to theft: nicking a copy of the *NME* is not as exciting as getting high on the dealer's stash. Or apply it to watching porn: titillation can now only be achieved from watching clips involving suction pumps, a cast of hundreds, and a length of hose.

Here's a further explanation of the Jekyll-to-Hyde transformation that can overcome a person once they've opened the door – just a crack – to temptation. The reward-hungry part of our brain experiences a loss of functional connectivity with the part that weighs up pros and cons. It means we're less able to control our base impulses.

How convenient.

In a blog post titled 'Two Yous', neuroscientist Marc Lewis suggests it's helpful to imagine the self as two people: one who anticipates the feel-good factor of getting high, and the other who knows it's a bad idea. Lewis aligns the psychology of *wanting* versus *abstaining* with two distinct brain states. *Wanting* activates the striatum, which initiates goal pursuit and forges a strong link with the orbitofrontal cortex (responsible for encoding the value of things) when a goal is in sight. *Abstaining* is associated with the dorsolateral prefrontal cortex, where reasonable decisions are made. Lewis calls it the bridge of the ship – its job is to stay true to our intended path.

'But addiction and other impulsive acts are accompanied by a loss in functional connectivity between the orbitostriatal alliance and the bridge of the neural ship,' he explains. 'A loss of connectivity simply means that activity (measured by an fMRI brain scan) in one region becomes less correlated with activity in the other region.'

Dopamine is involved, as you might imagine: this process is the result of changes in dopamine signalling, and activity in the mesolimbic circuit. It means that, for someone who's a problematic drug user, there's a disconnect between desire and reason. 'When pictures of drug paraphernalia are flashed on a screen, addicts show a surge of activity in the orbitostriatal region and relatively less activity in the dorsolateral PFC,' he says. 'Some studies show this disconnect to become more severe with the length of the addiction. Other studies show the same disconnect when "normal" people surrender to tempting (but dumb) impulses. The disconnect is real. And when it happens, you become the unfettered, unconstrained child.'

And when the bender comes to an end and the orbitofrontal

cortex regains activity with the dorsolateral prefrontal cortex? The conscience returns. And with it, remorse, distress, self-reproach.

What if some people were actually born with dopamine deficiency? Some research, spearheaded by neuropsychopharmacologist Kenneth Blum, suggests that thirty per cent of the population of the US has what he calls Reward Deficiency Syndrome, which increases the risk of obsessive-compulsive, impulsive and addictive behaviours. The theory is that these people carry the D2A1 allele, which means they have insufficient numbers of D2 (dopamine) receptors in their brain, resulting in lack of dopamine-related reward.

It's a pretty well-accepted theory, actually – for explaining those who get severely dependent – but Blum's critics caution that there's no silver bullet for addiction, and that having the D2A1 allele might not be more of a risk factor than, say, being exposed to alcohol and drugs as a child. One professor, who preferred not to get into a public slanging match, tells me, 'Blum has packaged together something that people have been familiar with for a long time. There's no doubt that some people have dopamine deficiency for various reasons, including drug use itself, but when researchers take a piece of information and say "this is the answer", that's when we have problems. Is it a piece of the jigsaw? Yes. Is it the whole picture? No.'

If substance-use problems purely boiled down to genetics, says this professor, why would alcohol consumption go up and down related to price? Why would there be heavier alcohol consumption in the north-west of Australia compared to the south-east? Why would it change historically? 'Genetic studies can be relevant but they're often reductionist in the extreme,' he says. 'I mean, the fact that I like to wear brown jeans is genetically influenced.'

Another academic I discuss this with chips in, 'I'm over forty and so am at increased risk of cardiovascular disease. Does that mean I have Age Oversupply Syndrome?'

In any case, while neuroscientific theories can be extremely seductive, it's actually extremely difficult to test for dopamine deficiency. Blood and urine screening services that purport to do so can only test for levels in the body, which are entirely different from levels in the brain, which has its own transmitters. Only brain imaging could detect problematic levels, and dopamine MRI checks are not readily available to the public. What would be the point, anyway? If an individual could triumphantly claim that they undisputedly had dopamine deficiency and were to start their own DD fellowship, they would be blithely ignoring all the other environmental, psychological and cultural issues that will also have contributed to their substance use.

Sex, stealing, gambling and imbibing are all temporary fixes. Fuelled by unbearable emotions, they drown out internal clamour, but as long-term coping mechanisms they serve to do more damage. There are five behavioural stages that demonstrate an impulse-control disorder in full flight, and these stages are familiar in many kinds of compulsive behaviour. There's an impulse; rising tension; pleasure from acting; relief; and guilt – although not everyone experiences that final stage.

The discomfort of that mounting tension and indecision cannot be underestimated. The brain hates cognitive dissonance – that jarring feeling of conflicting desires. If a person is trying to prevent themselves from acting on a harmful impulse – such as a spending spree or shooting up – and finds themselves in a tug of war between those duelling desires for days, weeks, or even years, the relief in making even the 'wrong' decision can be immense. Harm-reduction pioneer Professor Alan Marlatt advised 'urge surfing' in these scenarios: pausing to visualise a craving or impulse as an ocean wave, then riding with that wave as it rises and crests, until it diminishes and harmlessly reaches the shore.

If I'd known all this when I was younger, I might have urge-surfed my brain through each impulse to steal, or at least tried to play out the scenario in my mind to its logical conclusion – being under suspicion, being moved to lie to cover my tracks – which was a tactic never tried.

Karma got me five years after the Squatopia-stealing episode, anyway. I'd been casting around for a bit of trouble after the demise of a wonderful, healthy two-year relationship, and I happened across a London pub that would provide me with everything I needed for a bad time.

Inside the double doors, the scene was lit up with a golden glow. The DJ spun three-chord rockabilly tracks that it was important to be able to identify, but the main activity was ducking flying pint glasses. The aggrieved landlord, a bristling little man with a moustache, watched the clientele file off to the toilets in twos and had a smile for no one. The women – straight out of Russ Meyer movies with their cat-eye scowls and tight pedal-pushers – mingled separately for an authentic 1950s feel and got involved in loud kitchen-sink dramas. I wasn't into that segregation of the sexes, but I liked the idea of being the blowsy dame in a James Ellroy or Jim Thompson novel and, anyway, I knew I was a boy's girl and could easily cross enemy lines.

Excellent, I thought, handing over two shiny pounds for my first pint of cider. Nobody will ever notice my behaviour here. Furthermore, there will always be someone worse.

Each weekend, as the rudimentary cider-and-ecstasy-pill cocktails took hold, I realised with increasing clarity that this pub was quite serious about its pulp-fiction violence. One girl shoved another into a toilet bowl with such force that the thing cracked in two. I saw at least two other people – one male, one female – get sucker-punched so hard, without warning, that they needed titanium plates fitted in their faces. Yet I wasn't inclined to leave my seat.

One night, a substantial sum went missing at a house party connected to the scene, and I was falsely accused of being the thief, by a woman who disliked my 'boy's girl' ethos. In this tinderbox, the rumours exploded. People I thought were as neutral as Switzerland suddenly turned their backs when I asked for a light. Those who hadn't yet taken their own turn in the village stocks thrilled behind splayed fingers. As for those who had, they experienced a dopamine-rich spike of schadenfreude; the pleasure in somebody else's misfortune, which researchers at Japan's National Institute of Radiology have discovered sets the reward pathway a-tingle.

By now I'd completely curbed my stealing tendencies – *It's not for you*, a voice would remind me with finality if my eyes alighted on something – which made me all the more aware that other people in this scene had not. One friend nicked my change off the kitchen table, which just fascinated me in its obviousness. Another crept into the darkened room of her friend's flatmate and scooped some notes from the dresser as the girl lay in bed and watched, later denying it far and wide. Women's purses went missing out at clubs, or were emptied while they were on the dance floor, all the time.

Did they have depression, obsessive-compulsive disorder, dopamine deficiency, low serotonin, or a loss in functional connectivity between the orbitostriatal alliance and the bridge of the neural ship? Or did they just want a bit more cider money? I'll never know. Once again, it was time for me to go.

11

THE GEOGRAPHICAL

Running away to the edge of the world and falling off

Switching hemispheres comes under what's known as 'doing a geographical'. In addiction terms, that's what you do when you run away from your problems, which then turn out to be tied to your tail. But at least you can experience a more temperate climate as you let things blow over.

I was sick to death of myself, and I knew that if I stayed in London my chances of ever changing would be nil. So I left. In the years since, the pub social scene in which I'd spent all my lost weekends, itself lost many members: to heart attack, kidney failure, jail, suicide and a fatal stabbing.

So when, in 2006, I found myself descending through crepuscular rays over Sydney Harbour, the outline of which I had traced with my finger in brochures in the months leading up to that moment, I was overcome with such joy and relief that the hum of the Qantas engines transformed into a divine chorus.

I should introduce you to my travel-mate, Tim. I was as surprised as anyone when I married an Australian. Stories about

Tim had originally filtered to me through an angry friend. Clare complained that she'd gone out drinking with this boy and he'd had a matchbox full of pills in his pocket that he kept tucking into. As the night progressed he became more and more incoherent, until she finally had it out with him on some bridge, the wind whipping her hair. 'I told him, "Tim, if you take one more I'm going home."' At this, he popped another in his mouth.

This bloke sounded interesting. When I finally met him, after Clare had cooled down, I liked him a lot. He was lanky and lolloping, with sketchy tattoos and the limpid brown eyes of a sponsor-a-child orphan. He carried a worn paperback of some crumbling Russian poet and nothing else that couldn't be stuffed into his tight jeans, through which you could clearly make out his bon scotts. We were running late to see a band play, so he drained his pint in one. When Clare declined to do the same, he drained hers, too. It was on.

After that night, Tim and I started criss-crossing the city to see each other. We would buy booze from the bottle shop before a hard day's labour – Stella for him, Strongbow for me – and drink it on the train. What a kindred spirit. Of course we fell in love.

The flip side was I'd never met someone with such a pronounced death wish. Tim kept burning up and breaking out in weird rashes from head to foot, refusing to seek hospital treatment. He'd nearly died a few times before I met him, from his exotic Newtown lifestyle. His torso was sliced and potted with scars from where his ribcage had been cranked open and his lungs drained and reinflated, the hallmark of double pneumonia. I lived in constant fear the same would happen on my watch and I'd have to make that call to his mother. Just as my family loved Tim, his family loved me. In fact, many of them seemed to think I'd saved him from certain death, which I would politely laugh off while trying to appear straight. Mushrooms were huge that year.

Like me, Tim was volatile. The bloke could switch into maudlin mode in a heartbeat (if I heard the strains of Elliott Smith as I put my key in the latch, I'd do an about-turn and retreat to the pub), or would rise up from corpse position and lecture someone on their taste in music with a fervour last seen at the Nuremberg Rally. Our fights were legendary. Since our converted warehouse was split-level, we could never retire to a different room and bang the door behind us. Instead we'd each take a storey and bombard one another with missiles: balls of socks hurled up from the peanut gallery and, in retaliation, an entire rail of dresses hurtled down the stairs from the top deck. Tim liked making points loudly and persistently; I liked avoiding points. He liked to swing from the pipe twenty foot up to freak out guests; I liked to storm out. But we were just warring siblings, with no genuine intention to hurt or maim.

Over the next five years together, my drinking had peaks and troughs, but it was never out of control. Nor did I get sad when drunk anymore, although often my eyes streamed, as if to imply I *should* be unhappy. I just carried on talking to people as normal, vaguely waving at my face and referring to 'getting rid of the toxins'.

Methodically, I began to prune away any behaviour that had never served me well, tweaking myself into a better friend, daughter and human being. Like a grown-up, I had got married, and I felt the very act had given me amnesty from public opinion. *See? Someone married me. And now I am no longer a threat to you or myself.* Maybe we would settle in the same town as Tim's family, who had many wild and woolly kids. We would have the suburban weatherboard, the pool, the SUV, the double barbecue, the son and daughter with limpid brown eyes, and the occasional messy house party to remember who we once were. Then I would finally be able to cast off my old skin.

'What did you get up to on the weekend, Jen? Bet you went hard, eh?'

That was Greg, my boss and the publisher of a music magazine that I'd moved to Melbourne to edit. He's a dyed-in-the-wool newshound who, in the 1980s, was stationed in posh hotels around the globe, sticking his bar bill on expenses. Even when on home turf, journalists like him were expected to smoke at their desks then pass out beneath them.

Times had changed: it was now all about web-traffic reports, advertorial, and carefully rationed cab charges. Even so, Greg liked to wander over to my desk of a morning to get the general gist that a heavy-drinking session had recently been enjoyed. He practically wistfully sniffed the air.

I loved my job. Our small team all cared for that magazine, and pored over every photo and layout. I was also a control freak, checking in daily when I was on annual leave, demanding that every page be run past me, and generally wasting hours writing long, self-righteous emails to colleagues I considered to be difficult, an activity I only lost interest in doing once I had stopped drinking. I lost all urge for bullet points then, come to think of it. Once, mid-meeting, one of the senior staff was moved to comment on the egotistical power trip I was on, but I knew it must be projection on his part. I mean, I had to dash off to the pub to knock back a wine just to speak in that boardroom in the first place; how could I possibly have an ego?

Now that I no longer work for Greg, we go for lunch. He hates the idea of a journalist breaking the fourth wall and bleating about their problems in a book, which is funny because loads of addiction memoirs are by journalists; just the tip of the ice luge being Caroline Knapp's *Drinking: A Love Story*; A.A. Gill's *Pour Me*; Tania Glyde's *Cleaning Up*; Alice King's *High Sobriety*; Ann Marlowe's *How to Stop Time: Heroin from A to Z*; Luke Williams' *The Ice Age*; Marya Hornbacher's *Wasted*; and Rosie Boycott's *A Nice Girl Like Me*. Anyway, Greg would surely be secretly chuffed to know I got away with murder in my final, fourth year at the magazine, when my drinking reached its glorious zenith.

Being editor, I could delegate work then slip downstairs to the food court in the afternoon, which counted a few bars among its outlets. I'd get some valuable 'me time' with a dirty martini, and read over some pages. That was after the two glasses of wine with my pub lunch and just before knocking off to head straight to the bottle shop for a traveller. Having chugged the traveller – a UDL or a miniature wine, perhaps – I'd pinball from pub to pub on my route back to the marital home, which should have taken forty minutes, but usually took a couple of hours.

Once home, I'd head straight for the freezer and unscrew the lid of the honey vodka, just a trickle or three in a glass. Tim would look up from the sofa, nursing a beer in one hand and a Stephen Spender paperback in the other. He'd keep his face steady, torn between disapproval and not wanting to jeopardise his own drinking freedom.

Tim had never wanted to move to Melbourne from Sydney, so things were pretty fraught. He felt I'd put my career before him, which offended his socialist ethos. All the sneering about me being a 'careerist' had got a bit Rik-Mayall-in-*The Young Ones*. Now we were drinking separately. But I wasn't alone.

I've had a few drinking buddies who have encouraged my form, but Alexandra catapulted me to top of the premiership table. We met at a boozy soiree of women in publishing and within minutes she had whipped the laughter from my lungs. Alex's lust for life had taken her to far-flung places as a travel writer. She'd tumbled into volcanic sinkholes, talked her way out of being human-trafficked at the Chechen border, streaked in front of a televised audience of millions, and tried to bait crocodiles around her hometown in Far North Queensland with a frozen chicken dangled from the back of a tinny. She had a perpetual cigarette at her lips, and – being half-Russian – a great appreciation of vodka. The lunacy of our conversation inflated my brain like a balloon, then let it go, to zigzag madly around the bar.

So when we needed a subeditor, I recruited her for the magazine; mostly because she was an excellent writer whose inventive turns-of-phrase were nicked by everyone, but also because, if I loudly mentioned in the office that I was going to browse the newsagent downstairs, she'd dart into the lift and meet me at the Irish pub.

Increasingly, I was keeping my own hours and waking up in the spare room at home. Alex's relationship hit strife at the same time as mine, and we spent more and more time out drinking as an evasive tactic. With her loopy grin and fascination with people, she had the knack of making you feel like the only girl in the bar, although that wasn't true. Whenever I went to buy a round and rushed back with our drinks to continue the delirium, she'd be embroiled in conversation with the absolute worst person in the room. I'd always get that Simon and Garfunkel song 'Cecilia' in my head: I'd come back to bed and someone had taken my place.

Even so, I was delighted that I'd found one of those rare friends: the friend that is as bad as you. We were unable to look at each other half the time, for fear of disintegrating into snot-stringing idiocy. Beneath that, there was a curious aggressiveness, like stags clashing antlers. We'd rip at each other's stockings, barge each other in the corridor, shove each other into flowerbeds and dump bags of potato chips over each other's heads. But it felt productive. Down the pub one night we hatched a plan for a book together and within weeks had five major publishers vying for it.

Our days and nights soon became a cycle of booze-fuelled daring and double daring. If either of us was ever attempting to have a 'good day', the other would soon nip it in the bud. In emails later, analysing our drinking, Alex described our 'frenzied hallucination', 'deranged infatuations' (with local bartenders, usually), and our goading each other on with 'great dedication and compulsion'. She'd kept a journal of our movements and conversations, somehow filing them whenever she got home. I'd just scribble stuff down on scraps of paper and leave them in pubs.

Everything was mortifying and hilarious. We were creeping up on our mid-thirties; slovenly old crones; despicable biddies with flapping maws and splayed elbows. We were Selma and Patty from *The Simpsons*. But at least we had each other.

You have been waiting patiently for a rock bottom. Here it is. It came only for me.

Creeps have a tendency to return to the scene of the crime. They join search parties, hover at taped-off areas, and shoot the breeze with the cops. That was my take on things when I opened my laptop to find a Friends Reunited message in my inbox from Adrian: 'Remember me?'

Yeah, remember him? He'd used me as his own personal sex-ed class when he was in high school and I was seven. I sat on the couch and stared at those two words for a while, thinking: 'Here we go, then.'

Adrian would have been nearly forty by then. I hadn't seen him since a wedding when I was twenty. A reassuring wrap of speed had been concealed in my bridesmaid's shoe as I solemnly circumnavigated the church in front of him. Later, at the reception, he followed me around like a bad smell under the puzzled gaze of his wife. 'Hello, Jenny ... *Jenny!* ... Hello, Jenny.' I had expected him to avoid me, but instead he seemed to gloat. He quizzed a relative I was hovering around for safety: 'She doesn't seem to want to talk to me, does she?'

That night I'd retired to my hotel room as soon as protocol would allow, and thumped it senseless. Now I went to his profile page, which had a list of his employers and extracurricular interests. These included supporting children's charities and working with kids who were the same age I had been ('changing lives, one adventure at a time!'). I actually knew all this already, because I'd been keeping tabs on him on the internet for some time. A few years earlier I'd called the organisation he volunteered for and hesitantly expressed my concern, torn between not wanting to incriminate somebody who could be innocent these days and not doing my duty. I requested reassurance that no adult was ever left unsupervised around children, especially him.

Really, though, I'd let him off the hook. He had been an adolescent boy, not yet grown into whatever full-size character he was destined to be. The abuse had come with the extra complication that, despite our age difference, we were all 'the children' in the words of the adults, and so I had dismissed the night visits as one of those secret children things, which was just bad luck for me. All the terrible times in my life since, I reasoned, I had inflicted upon myself.

Yet here he was, appearing in my inbox years after he'd lost touch with the rest of my family, as if he thought he should have been there all along. I analysed my notion of what a pedophile was. Mainly it seemed to be a media construct. It emphasises the other, one who is not like us. It accompanies photographs of dilapidated men with child-catcher faces and stained leisurewear. But look at the stats: seventy to ninety per cent of women seeking treatment for substance use have been abused. That's a lot of shuffling, crazy-eyed perverts among us, then, is it? Where are they all hiding?

The truth is most children will be abused by opportunists: the married relatives, the family friends, the pillars of the community, the good guys, the neighbourhood teenagers who want to improve their prowess ... all of whom would consider themselves to be sexually 'into' their own age bracket, unless they'd had a few drinks or a child was blatantly putting it out there. I wonder how many kids since the 1960s have been silenced by those 'stranger danger' campaigns that implied molestation occurred when you were offered a glimpse of some puppies and then bundled into a van? Actually, only eleven per cent of perpetrators of violent crimes against children are strangers, and sex offences are the crimes least likely to involve strangers.

Since I was used to partners not wanting to discuss my past – the past is the past, after all – I isolated further from Tim; but Alex was supportive, and my mum leaped into action. It takes, on average, twenty-two years before someone speaks out about sexual abuse. She and I had finally had *that* conversation four years before Adrian's inbox message, when I was twenty-nine – so, bang on schedule. She was horrified that she hadn't picked up on it. Now she made enquiries with social services, who opined that child-on-child sexual activity wasn't unusual if the children were siblings or the same age, but was officially abuse with this age gap.

I needed to act, too; to not feel passive. You can assimilate a bad experience; you can make it become your persuasion, your character quirk, your movie script, your sexual fetish, even. But these are your own clever methods of regaining control. To have that power taken away again is devastating.

I pitched a feature to a newspaper about the ethical difficulty of the situation, with quotes to come from the police, psychologists and child-protection agencies. It was therapy-by-assignment, and my involvement was way too immediate to be proper, but nevertheless the editor quickly commissioned it. Briefly, I had a sense of purpose.

Within a few weeks, I submitted the first draft. The editor asked if I would meet one of her colleagues in Melbourne for a coffee. The inference was plain: to make sure I was mentally well enough to withstand the pressure of publication. It was a humiliating scenario, since the colleague and I both worked for the same company, but the editor was correct to implement it. That kind of story can feel like it might detonate in your hand, as might the author.

The conversation in the cafe must have gone smoothly, because my next email from the editor read: 'Make it more graphic so people can see why you're angry.' Within a week, though, I was walking into the medical centre close by the newspaper offices. The moment I crossed the threshold, I cried. I told the doctor that I couldn't stop drinking.

She was a kind doctor. We browsed the internet together, looking at alcohol substitutes, such as Campral, which negates the effects of alcohol on brain chemistry once the individual has quit, and naltrexone, which reduces the cravings and the pleasurable effects of drinking, but neither would address my distress. In the end, she settled on an antidepressant.

I took the pills and didn't drink for five weeks; not until my parents came to Australia for a visit. One look at the goon box Dad had placed on the kitchen table, and I decided to join them in a cheeky little wine. The medication didn't react well to alcohol. If I drank too much, I'd projectile vomit.

Some weeks later, I was in Sydney for a work trip. It was forty degrees. I stayed with a friend and spent the morning after a drinking session throwing up in his toilet, then slumping back onto the tiles. My mobile rang; it was the newspaper editor. She was very sorry but she had changed her mind. It was an awkward call to make. She just wasn't sure the readers would be sympathetic.

I didn't argue. I ended the call, went back into the bathroom, and vomited some more.

I was increasingly absent at work, either going to visit a psychoanalyst, or wandering to Fitzroy Gardens to drink a UDL in the protective arms of a fig tree.

Seeing the psychoanalyst accounted for some of the increased distress. Our weekly sessions had a focus on delving deep into the past rather than providing tools for the present, and it cracked a schism in me so wide I felt as though I was walking about with one foot in this world, and one in another. I've since heard that embarking on a course of psychoanalysis before quitting substances is a bad idea. This therapist was opening cans of worms and redecorating the inside of my head with them, and I didn't have the resilience to deal with it.

It was weird but, as I got progressively worse, Tim got progressively better – quite the opposite to our opening stances. It was like we had politely waited our turns. Even weirder, I'd become a lightweight. Less than a bottle of civilised white wine now had me falling over, blacking out, and forgetting how to speak. The latter was greatly concerning me. My vocabulary would be chomped away in fifteen-minute segments until all I was left with was: *kkgghhh.* So much for building tolerance; at some point, I'd slipped into reverse and stepped on the accelerator. Thankfully, I never actually learned to drive.

When I was in the office I was more often than not sat on the toilet, where I'd shake with my head in my hands. I always wore black: black pencil skirt, black shirt, to hide the sweat that trickled down my sides and traversed my torso. My internal organs felt like boil-in-the-bag chicken. The sheets were soaked at night. My kidneys ached, my nose itched, my mouth was pocked with ulcers. I suffered constant nausea, diarrhoea, prickling nerves, breathlessness and fatigue. My hand muscles jumped like marionettes, and my eye ticked to its own beat.

Worse was what Alex and I had labelled 'The Fear': the impending sense of doom that comes from excessive drinking. Alcohol interferes with the level of serotonin in the brain, which can cause anxiety and depression. When the sedative effect wears off, the central nervous system swings the other way, bringing a quickened pulse. Plummeting blood sugar during a hangover causes further shakiness and confusion. The Fear might also be attributed to adrenal fatigue, which causes alcohol intolerance and also, because of heightened cortisol levels, feelings of dread.

There's some evidence that heavy alcohol use can actually prolong fearfulness. One 2012 experiment by scientists at the National Institute on Alcohol Abuse and Alcoholism (NIAAA) exposed one group of mice to regular doses of alcohol (the equivalent of twice the legal driving limit), while a control group received none. Both groups were then conditioned to fear a noise that they would hear while being given electric shocks. The next step was to remove the shocks but keep the noise. Those mice who hadn't been exposed to alcohol quickly learned to stop fearing the noise. The 'alcoholic' group retained the fearful memory for longer, still freezing in their tracks upon hearing it.

Alex was suffering her own set of physical ailments – endless stomach parasites, greying skin and a rattling, pleuritic cough. She was starting to beg time out from drinking, which I couldn't possibly stand for. I'd try and goad her into it, by waving a bottle under her nose, for instance, but sometimes she'd hold strong. What a betrayal.

Those nights my bad chaperone wasn't out with me, I'd make a complete fool of myself, saying all the wrong things to the worst-possible people. I'd know this because I'd find notes scribbled down on a sheet of paper in my handbag. Just awful things in quotation marks, really. I was getting increasingly confused when I drank, often having to leave by nine o'clock, sometimes not recognising my surroundings when I swerved through the double doors into the night air. Maybe the findings of neuroscientist Susan Tapert, back in chapter three, can account for this: girls who drink heavily at a young age damage the white matter of their brain, which is responsible for – among other things – recognition of surroundings. One evening I found myself at a pub table with a veteran musician and noticed he was teetotal. I stared at him throughout round after round, dying to ask why. And, more importantly, *how*. Some thin strand of etiquette prevented me from enquiring while drunk – I think – and instead I shit my pants on the walk home.

But I couldn't stop, could I? Who stops drinking forever? I couldn't conceive of that kind of future. Better to get things under control. One of my friends had seen a hypnotherapist and successfully quit smoking. I booked in and told the guy my predicament as I reclined in his curious leather chair.

'I need you to tell me I can only have two glasses of wine, nothing else,' I said, lying back. 'And only after six p.m.'

He laced his fingers together.

'And,' I added, 'not at all if it's in any way job-related.'

'It's not going to work,' he said, frowning at me. 'I can only collaborate with your own willpower, and you clearly don't want to stop.'

'It's fine, I'll pay you anyway.'

The hypnotherapist agreed to attempt to jack into my unconscious brain but, oddly, the more sessions we had, the heavier I drank. It was like some inner imp had seen my efforts and raised me a rebellion.

'Do you think your drinking got worse when you met me?' Alex asked one day, looking troubled. 'Quite a few people have said that.'

No, I told her. That was the weird thing. I'd been worse than this, much worse. I'd been left half-naked in an alleyway; I'd been psychotically paranoid; and I'd subjected myself to more humiliations. It's just that it had never felt this wretched. I was thirty-four. I no longer wanted to roll with the punches and wade back in for another swing. I didn't want to keep dyeing my hair to go incognito after a particularly unfortunate incident, or never wear a certain dress again because of the awful association it now held.

Some doomsday clock was ticking; the certainty of death had settled upon me like a shroud. Maybe I would wander, confused, in front of a tram. Maybe I would be throttled in an alley on my way home. Maybe I would skid in my socks, dancing alone to Kate Bush with a wine glass in my hand, and hit my head on the dressing table. Or maybe I'd wank myself to death. I did keep waking up in front of my laptop screen, the incriminating evidence before me.

Alex was backing off. I was writing her increasingly long, rambling emails, obsessing over fears and people, and people I was fearful of, which was everyone. Later, when I'd quit drinking, I read those emails again and didn't recognise myself. My Facebook page was deactivated and activated, deactivated and activated, like a nervous tic. I was petrified of people finding out who I really was. I'd tried to reinvent my life as editor, wife and mother-to-be, yet by night I was shooting my mouth off to every fool with a bar stool.

'Those people aren't your friends,' was all Tim could rouse himself to say. He and I were now in a very bad way. I had realised that to have children would be a mistake. I'd never heard that biological clock tick. I had been trying to mould myself into a person I was not, with Tim in the centre of my grand design. He'd pinned his hopes on a faithless lush. When I finally talked to him about it, he sat on the sofa and silently wiped away his tears.

Rock bottom minus four weeks. I was sent out on an unusual assignment. The Black Saturday bushfires had devastated the Kinglake–Marysville region of Victoria, reducing towns to a rubble of corrugated iron and chimney stacks. One hundred and seventy-three dead; 2029 homes destroyed. A popular band was going to play to the displaced people, who were all camped like refugees on the football ovals. I was asked if I would be the journalist to cover it.

We congregated in an office in Melbourne and were briefed on the state of each township, before starting our convoy north. The night before I had gone to the bottle shop and stocked up on miniature bottles of vodka, which I had secreted about my person so that they wouldn't clink together and give me away. The band members were silent as we drove past the first army roadblock, and the gravity of the situation really hit us. They were nervous about how they would be received. They hoped to raise morale, just a little, but would their gesture be appreciated by people who had lost their homes and families?

One of the band, who I had clocked as being more antsy than the others, claimed to need a piss break as we trundled past a pub, so we stopped. On my way back from the ladies' room I saw him furtively knock back a beer at the bar, and I gave him a sympathetic smile. No need to join him. I'd just sunk a miniature in the toilet cubicle.

The road into the first town was flanked by trees like spent matches. As the band set up on the football oval, I detoured to a portaloo. I magicked a Smirnoff out of the pocket in the strap of my laptop bag and downed it in one. My eyes met the eyes in the little acrylic mirror on the back of the door. They were wide and wobbly, like a kid on acid.

Why you? Why do you get to drink?

Back out on the oval, I walked past a makeshift canteen tent, diverting my gaze from the family sat around one table with their heads in their hands. At each further township, more devastation. I drank carefully, never exceeding the point that would tip me over from having a stable constitution of alcohol to being noticeably tipsy. But what made me so special?

It hit me that week. I wasn't just in despair; I was entirely dependent on alcohol to function. Walking home one night, I put my headphones in and listened to the hypnotherapist's podcast. As the positive affirmations rumbled on, great, rucking sobs heaved from my guts. *You are feeling more confident in yourself than ever before ... Notice how people greet you positively when you walk into the room.* But he was wrong about me.

Outside our house, I sat on the step to finish crying, then went inside to Tim. He was stood over the stove, stirring, and stopped when I buried my face in his shoulder. We stayed like that for a while.

15 March 2009. I woke up in the spare room; not unusual. I was still dressed, my bag upended on the floor. When I ransacked my

memory there was nothing doing beyond six o'clock the night before, so I reached down to fish out the scrap paper I'd put in my bag before leaving the house. On this, as ever, I would have scrawled important fragments of conversation, particularly as it was a work-related event.

Not this time. Needing water, I swung my legs out of bed and stopped. My knees were scraped raw.

Alex was away, in Cambodia. *Or this would never have happened!* Creeping outside so as not to wake Tim in the main bedroom, I rang a friend and summoned her to the nearest pub, panicking over the dots I was joining: a girl sobbing, someone telling me to fuck off, loss of speech, looming faces, being shaken by the shoulders. Not enough information; but also too much.

For once, my friend wasn't laughing. With glazed eyes, I knocked back multiple red wines, hard. A thought was forming, and then an absolute certainty. I had exhausted every option in regards to cutting down: professional help, medication, hypnosis. *So it's over.* Thirty-four years old – and I was done. The relief was overwhelming.

PART THREE

WOMAN'S LIB

12

52 OBSERVATIONS

A week-by-week account of my first year after quitting

WEEK ONE. I'm unwilling to take time off work and relinquish my grip to drop anchor in detox and rehab. Nor do I feel I need to, since my level of withdrawal doesn't place me in any danger. I find an Alcoholics Anonymous meeting in my lunchbreak and am pleasingly bamboozled by the secret language and rituals. The Freemasons may not take me, but AA will.

The program also involves lots of lists. You list your character defects, keep an inventory of your behaviour, and examine your motives. At night you write a gratitude list. In short, AA is an ingenious distraction from drinking. There is now no room in my head for anything other than: 'Who are these people and what are they on about?' And: 'Where's my list?'

WEEK TWO. I have reinvented the wheel. There's a feeling of wonder, as if I've grown another head. It's a door opening into another universe of possibility ... *I can do anything*. It's identical to the feeling when I first discovered booze. I don't care what people think anymore.

Need cake and chocolate through an intravenous drip, thanks to a sharp deprivation of sugar via alcohol. Every time the snacks trolley comes around at work, I guzzle another energy drink.

At night, I'm dropping instantly into a deep, dreamless sleep, waking up with a dead arm and pool of drool when the alarm goes off. I no longer wake with the sheets soaked in sweat. I no longer have to sprint for the toilet in the morning.

WEEK THREE. Alex comes back from her trip to Cambodia, expecting to pick up the hilarity where we left off. I'm expecting a Bollywood-style reaction to the fact that I've stopped drinking and my life has changed forever. Neither happens. We both uneasily insist our relationship will remain the same and that we'll go out and do ... crafty things. Nice things, like making macramé potholders and taking high tea and ... stuff.

Tim and I split up. He walks out of our house with one suitcase, saying he doesn't need anything else.

WEEK FOUR. In one month I have found a mortgage broker, started driving lessons, bought a casserole dish, fixed my teeth, done all my tax paperwork and taken out health insurance. People at AA warn me this is my honeymoon period.

WEEK FIVE. I'm feeling cocky. I've seen the light and I'm absolved of all past behaviour – hooray. My 'shares' at meetings all hit home runs in their impact and styling, so I try to blend in a touch of pathos and humility so as not to make the sad sacks feel bad. I don't like the semantics of recovery – 'recovery', 'alcoholic', 'disease' – but I'll say potato and they can say potarto.

I feel smug when I give concise instructions to cab drivers and put my key straight in the front door's lock on first attempt. Everything is a 'first'. Taking a lunchbreak without two glasses of white. Interviewing bands without the preparatory Dutch courage. Making a train journey without a miniature bottle of wine.

WEEK SIX. Dopamine release is all about goal-related behaviour. I'm a proactive, productive woman, and going to the pub always had purpose: I would be striving for the perfect level of drunkenness. Now I have no purpose in pubs. My existence there is pointless, and a weekend on a bar stool is a weekend wasted. Because of this I never see Alex outside of work; and anyway, I don't want to talk about anything other than AA, which torpedos any chance of mutually enjoyable conversation. You quit drinking to stop being a selfish person, then enrol in a twelve-step program of self-scrutiny for the rest of your life.

WEEK SEVEN. Everyone at AA is chasing epiphanies and studying to be a drug and alcohol counsellor. Most don't tell the General Public they don't drink, because the General Public generally reacts as if you've told them you have an inoperable bum tumour. That's funny, because I do feel like I'm walking around with a secret tumour. I wonder how many other people have secret tumours. For a journalist, I'm coming late to the idea that everybody's got a story.

WEEK EIGHT. I take a train into the country and buy a 1950s weatherboard house within three days. People at AA tell me you shouldn't do *anything* in your first twelve months sober, but shouldn't we ride the momentum? A major life shake-up is the perfect opportunity to change everything else, and rarely does such an impetus come along. I am fleshing out this idea of a new girl. She lives in the country. She drives a ute. Her wardrobe runs from denim to plaid. She hasn't got her licence yet but she contracts a local hoon to show her how to do burnouts in his V8.

WEEK NINE. Alex has replaced me, already. Already! She's pulled the art director into her tractor beam, and they're away on adventures, guffawing, colluding, and bunking off for lengthy fag breaks. I'm left sucking lemons. It's like being cheated on in your own home. We are supposed to be promoting our book together and we can't even look at each other. I want her to acknowledge the turmoil I'm going through. She wants me to chill the fuck out. Although, at AA they warn you not to presume what other people want.

WEEK TEN. I feel ten years older. I look gaunt, and my eyeballs are like little pissholes in the snow from uncontrollable crying over nothing. My AA shares are impotent and scattered. Why am I telling these people anything, when for the first time in a couple of decades I feel the need for privacy? I feel as if I'm going through twelve-step puberty and rebelling; how embarrassing. When you stop running, everything catches up with you. Shame, mainly. Sometimes I want to leave myself on a church doorstep or check myself into a home for disturbed young ladies so I don't have to worry about anything. Maybe I should have taken some time off work.

WEEK ELEVEN. I pong like an old hot-water bottle, and Dr Google is offering no answers – although I assume from the smorgasbord of pimples on my face and back that it's down to a release of some hardcore toxins. I'm down two dress sizes (thank you, fingers) and I no longer have to wear black, since my midriff isn't drenched in sweat. But my face is ablaze with raging battalions of bumps and rashes; I can't stand to look at myself. My teeth ache from grinding at night. Some days I wake up with a phantom hangover. Eventually I figure out this is fatigue. How did I cope with being hungover *and* tired?

WEEK TWELVE. Three months. Surely time enough to be ready to return to Splendour in the Grass, the festival at which Alex and I got booted out of every area and a few surrounding pubs the year before. This year we're setting each other's teeth on edge; no wonder she keeps turning her head and swigging from a hip flask when she thinks I'm not looking. The bloke she's with keeps coming into my room at the beach house and telling me he's worried about his drinking. He's so drunk he keeps trailing off mid-sentence and looking confused. Out in the lounge room Alex is playing the same Russian drinking song over and over.

My mood doesn't improve the next day. Whenever I spot a dinner plate with a bit of coke on it, I rinse it under the tap and put it in the dishwasher. Someone's got to clean up around here.

WEEK THIRTEEN. Getting a strong urge to retreat, bid everyone adieu – and not even in a melodramatic way. Still, a reasonable voice keeps asking me if it might be okay to switch to some light drug use, perhaps. It points to the twelve-step motto that you should not take anything from the neck up as evidence that shelfing a pill up the rear end would be acceptable. Then someone at AA to whom I triumphantly point out this loophole tells me it's anything that *affects* you from the neck up.

WEEK FOURTEEN. I confess to Alex that everything feels surreal and I'm worried I'm talking gibberish all the time. She writes me a sweet email expressing concern and wondering if I should take some time off to 'absorb all the changes and the amazing things you've done this year. Just potter around and make yourself a little nesty nook.' I interpret it as a plot to overthrow me at the magazine. Among all the impurities my body is purging come these impurities of mind.

WEEK FIFTEEN. 'You're too thin,' Alex says during a fag break at work. We still have these four-minute moments.

'I don't know why – I'm not throwing up or anything.'

Lie.

I'm shocked by the strength of my repulsion towards her. My body clenches when she comes in, bringing with her the smell of cigarettes and booze. It's like I've become allergic. She comes in to work later and later, I'm sure of it. We never used to be that loose, did we? Maybe we did.

Our conversation gets heated and she calls me a 'passive-aggressive hypocrite', with unnerving accuracy. She's a great, joyous plum, and I've shrivelled into a raisin. 'You can apologise to me when you get to step nine,' she adds, exhaling smoke out of the corner of her mouth.

WEEK SIXTEEN. My hormonal craziness is off the scale. I hadn't even realised till now that I had women's issues – I thought they were for women-women. And I thought my chaos was always chemically induced. I've ditched my regular meeting after a humiliating hormonal spaz-out during a share ('I hate coming here!'), and I'm terrified it will happen at the new one.

WEEK SEVENTEEN. I was a much nicer person before I stopped drinking. Booze blunted my edges. I cruised, I went with the flow, I was extremely non-judgemental – provided you were like me. Now I've swung from toothy boozehound to judgemental puritan. I'm spuming with rage, quick to pour scorn, and highly suspicious. What was the point of stopping again?

WEEK EIGHTEEN. I'm having drinking dreams. You look down and see a glass in your hand, half empty. You realise you've been drinking all week. You're sodden with it. Everything is fucked. Sometimes I additionally dream I'm being watched by secret police. Not so secret, really – they're leaning against the wall in trench coats with their arms folded. Are they from AA?

WEEK NINETEEN. Can't stop playing Candy Crush on my phone, for a ding-ding-ding of dopamine in my brain. I'm like a rat with a lever. I'll play it for hours, or hop on every time I have a pause in a train of thought.

WEEK TWENTY. I'm sensing snorty bristling from some people when I explain that I'm not drinking because I no longer drink. It really seems to press a button – the 'you think that's bad' button. Everyone likes to think they have a worse drinking problem than everyone else. We can't all be right, but short of getting into a pissing contest about it we can only bristle and snort.

The thing is, it was only the same handful of people that ever saw me desperate and wretched, night after night after night. It's common among heavy imbibers and users to compartmentalise their lives, keeping family, old friends, and new friends apart in a Venn diagram that has the slimmest of intersections. They'll do that to the point that, when they finally quit, many of their acquaintances will express surprise that there was a problem at all.

WEEK TWENTY-ONE. Not even: glühweins on Berlin station platforms. Not even: hot toddies at outdoor ice rinks. Not even: champagne on trays at premieres. Not even: eggnog at Christmas.

WEEK TWENTY-TWO. Why did nobody sit me down last year and say, 'What the fuck are you doing?' My sponsor tells me they had their own problems.

WEEK TWENTY-THREE. Things were much funnier when my life was going tits up. My sense of humour has been sucked out of me through the straw of sobriety. One thing I'll say about the worst times of my life – they were hilarious.

WEEK TWENTY-FOUR. I can't bear the thought of hurting someone in a relationship again, but I equally can't bear the thought of being stranded in my head forever. My destiny is to sit on the front porch of my country home, alone, rather like Miss Havisham. But smoking.

WEEK TWENTY-FIVE. I go to a naturopath, who deduces my liver is angry. Angry? It's fucking furious. She prescribes some potions to reset my body. Zinc is good for zits (heavy metals and dioxins stored in your fat are released when you lose weight so quickly), P2 Detox Powder (broccoli sprout powder, potassium, and amino acids) fights hormonal disorders and liver damage, while withania improves energy and libido. Tall order.

WEEK TWENTY-SIX. I start sessions with a drug and alcohol service. The counsellor asks me if I feel worthless. No. Unlovable? No, I do all right. I concede that I don't seem to be the kind of person people feel protective towards and that just makes me want to disgust them even more.

Towards the end of our session she tells me that she has a real passion for working in drugs and alcohol.

'You're laughing?' she asks.

'It's just that for me it's an area of darkness and despair.'

'But more than any other area in psychiatry, you get to see people grow,' she says.

WEEK TWENTY-SEVEN. Alex and I now send each other long, overwrought emails about who ought to be fairer to whom, because in person we wind up giving each other the old 'talk to the hand'. We were never sentimental and soft with each other when we were great mates, so these expressions of emotion are like pulling teeth. I tell her my news in my head so I can hear her loopy laugh. She's sitting two feet away, and I really miss her.

WEEK TWENTY-EIGHT. Important findings: Tonic tastes a bit like gin and tonic, especially if you add juniper berries. Horseradish is a poor substitute for the mule-kick of alcohol. Non-alcoholic wine isn't that bad.

WEEK TWENTY-NINE. I am loitering in churches, searching for something to fill the spiritual void. Alcohol was like a relationship with a vengeful god. People at AA talk about the 'committee' in their heads. I've only got one voice but it's getting louder in direct defiance of my efforts. 'Sooner or later you'll probably end up killing yourself,' it sympathises. 'From the tree outside, for instance. Where would you get the rope?'

WEEK THIRTY. I am realising that there's no point in letting go of drugs or alcohol if you don't also let go of the excuses you used when taking them. I'm talking about my hard-done-by routine. But if I let go of the victim script – an internal one, but nevertheless very real – everything I've ever known myself to be will unravel. I'll have to start over again.

WEEK THIRTY-ONE. I'm lucky that a switch went off in my head the day I quit alcohol. I've never had to use willpower – or 'white-knuckle', as they say – because the desire to drink just went. That's lucky, because I couldn't go through all this again. I reckon I'd rather kill myself than relive the past thirty weeks of meetings, bubbling emotions, isolation and hormonal uprisings. That's the danger of AA in my eyes – at a time when all you have is hope, so much credence is placed on staying completely sober, and on starting again from scratch if you bust. The pressure is immense.

WEEK THIRTY-TWO. When I sniff whisky I no longer get goosebumps. I'm a little sad about that.

WEEK THIRTY-THREE. Drunk people don't trust me. They worry I'm judging them. They're right. I'm finding it incredibly liberating – finally being able to judge others. Their distrust is annoying as well, though. When I was still drinking, and I interviewed a musician who turned out to be five months' sober, I didn't think him a man-sized wowser. I thought he was a marvellous semi-mythical beast.

WEEK THIRTY-FOUR. I start an anonymous blog about quitting drinking. My slightly chilling vignettes rise out of the fog, then sink back again. I get correspondence from a woman in the US and another in Canada, both of whom have desperately been googling key words such as 'addiction' and 'women'. We become penpals. They're going to AA/NA, too. One of them talks to me about the men she fancies in the group. The other discloses her off-the-scale Red Bull addiction.

WEEK THIRTY-FIVE. I'm yet to utter an AA bumper sticker-ism but, for all their corniness, each hits the mark. AA's founder, Bill Wilson, was originally a salesman, and he was a genius marketeer. *The Big Book* reads like 1930s advertising copy. In the near-century since that was published, many more slogans and acronyms have been added to the pot.

Stinkin' thinkin'.

Hurt people hurt people.

Slippery souls need sober shoes.

Don't leave five minutes before the miracle happens.

Don't plant the fruit of today with the seeds of your past.

The only normal people are the ones you don't know very well.

A resentment is drinking poison and hoping someone else dies.

Take the cotton wool out of your ears and put it in your mouth.

Addictions are cunning, baffling, powerful and very, very patient.

All you get from sitting on the pity pot is a big ring around your bum.

It all works out in the end . . . if it hasn't worked out yet, it's not the end.

When you point a finger at someone there are three pointing back at you.

Yesterday is history, tomorrow is a mystery, and today is a gift ... that's why they call it the present.

WEEK THIRTY-SIX. A young woman at AA who takes me under her wing blows my mind with: 'What other people think of you is none of your business.' I ponder over this for ages, like Eeyore putting his burst balloon in and out of his Very Useful Pot, then I file it next to the equally useful: 'Don't waste your life waiting for other people to change.'

WEEK THIRTY-SEVEN. Another woman in a meeting describes trying to leave AA and then being the subject of an intervention by two female members, who employed standover tactics around her house. She seems grateful. But what if you didn't want to go back? Have the police ever had to be called on AA interventionists?

WEEK THIRTY-EIGHT. I have ploughed through every sobriety handbook I can find. This week I learn there's this thing called 'state-dependent learning'. If you learn to play pool in bars while drunk, you'll always play better when drunk. See also: everything else you learned to do while drunk since being perpetually drunk as a teenager.

WEEK THIRTY-NINE. Things AA wouldn't approve of that I'm okay with: Ordering tiramisu. Chocolate liqueurs. Drinking alcohol-free wine. Kissing a man with his mouth full of whisky. Smoking is considered to be okay, which is lucky because I've started again, having quit for four years. I used to only be able to smoke if I was also drinking, or I'd feel queasy. Turns out that it only required perseverance. Now I can feel it starting to fill all the places where I would usually just have wanted a drink. Fun fact: most people who die because of addiction and mental health issues do so from smoking.

WEEK FORTY. Ten months is a milestone for me – personally I couldn't see quitting as an achievement until I'd at least outlasted a pregnant woman; my competitive streak wouldn't allow that. The euphoria of the first few months has taken on a manic hue; I feel like a can of soda that's been shaken up. I thought I was the stoic one of my highly anxious family, but it turns out I just had a depressed central nervous system. I keep wondering what the point of living is, but my alcohol counsellor assures me I'm bang on time for existential feelings; that everything is running on course.

WEEK FORTY-ONE. I try to join an internet dating site but get rejected for failing their lengthy psychometric assessment. I have no idea who I am anymore, and their algorithms have sussed that out. I join a different internet dating site that doesn't screen applicants. Men's profiles specify 'no baggage'.

WEEK FORTY-TWO. In England, visiting my parents. My dad mutters to a relative: 'Apparently we're not drinking now.' I'd bought him a bottle of duty-free Scotch!

WEEK FORTY-THREE. Have a recurring amnesia dream that I've hacked someone to death and am going to be prosecuted.

I can't remember why or who, but I accept it to be true. While waiting to be sentenced I reason to myself: if I can't remember doing it, am I really guilty? Amnesia feels like a theme of my life: the blackouts, the loss of hours. When I think back on my childhood, those memories that aren't mysteriously smudged or erased and steeped in confusion have been largely overwritten with whatever escapist fantasy had been preoccupying me at the time.

WEEK FORTY-FOUR. A 2013 study by Professor Rajita Sinha, who's the founding director of the Yale Stress Center, found that the early stages of sobriety are often associated with higher levels of anxiety and greater emotional distress because feelings that have been anesthetised by substances are woken. The individual may not have even been aware that they had mental health issues, but now the issues stand knock-kneed and bare. Many of us women at AA are terrified of being crazy, or being seen as crazy. Still, a girl at one meeting points out that the Western world's main ailment is mental illness, while much of the rest of the world struggles with survival. My parents frequently remind me that in their day the most pressing concern was polio.

WEEK FORTY-FIVE. More chats with the AA newbie club for disturbed young ladies. Things we don't miss: Shitting our pants a bit. Being ropable with non-specific rage by the time we stagger to the front door. Needing to scrub out the insides of our heads. I love these women.

WEEK FORTY-SIX. I don't want my course of sessions with the drug and alcohol counsellor to end, so I start leaving her with cliffhangers as I stand and reach for my coat. 'Oh … I'm also throwing up.' Apparently this is quite a common tactic.

WEEK FORTY-SEVEN. When I was drinking I knew exactly what to eat that would aid the liver: beetroot, artichoke, B-vits. I'd read health magazines as if they were porn. Now I'm eating sugar all day and having a fried egg on instant noodles when I get home.

WEEK FORTY-EIGHT. I've been having regular phone calls with my ex, Tim. Sometimes I cop some flack, but we're making headway and his family is really good to me. I meet up with him in Sydney, where he lives now and is playing every weekend with his band as if he's got a new lease of life … or something.

WEEK FORTY-NINE. Actually enjoying Skyping my parents. I was such a punisher in the past as to be practically mute in our calls. Now, they're like a double act. They're Morecambe and Wise.

WEEK FIFTY. I write an account of my first year off booze for *The Big Issue*. Before I can press send, my employer indicates that I need to get permission from the client for whom we produce the music magazine. That annoys me – the client isn't my employer. The article gets read and upwardly referred many times. Eventually there's a grudging green light, but a clause in the email wants it noted that the client has expressed apprehension for my wellbeing, should it be published. For the second time in recent history I'm a journalist having my wellbeing discussed by an editorial department, and it strikes me there's a fine line between duty of care and paternalism. It feels a bit deflating, because achieving one year off the sauce is my biggest life achievement. A high-five would have done.

WEEK FIFTY-ONE. Alex leaves the magazine to catapult from continent to continent as a documentary maker. I realise that I've been so busy picking lint from my navel that I've missed all her recent launches and achievements. Now there's a six-foot void in the office.

WEEK FIFTY-TWO. At AA I get my one-year chip and a birthday cake. Over the past year I've spent my evenings purging myself of 100,000 words about drinking and quitting drinking, machine-gunning every waking thought into my laptop. That's okay. As long as it goes no further. Delete soon.

13

A WORD FROM MY SPONSOR

The female spaces in AA and NA

Author's note: All of the members depicted in this chapter are fictional, based on the kinds of stories that might be shared. This is with the exception of my faintly disguised sponsor, whom I have given the right of reply.

You could treat AA like a pick'n'mix and bounce from one meeting to another, all across the city, till you found something you liked. That's what I did. On arrival at each new group, I took a seat in the circle and did a scope of the room, of the men.

Nope. Nope. Nope. Maybe.

If a meeting didn't come with a smattering of hangdog ex-man-whores with downcast eyes – simply to pique my interest, you understand – I'd move on. It wasn't just me. Members often had to change meetings when an ill-advised fling resulted in them both needing to share. Your sponsor might thunder at you '*NO* relationships for the first year', but at the same time they wanted you to 'keep coming back'. So which was it?

You've got to find ways to entertain yourself in 'recovery'. You're spending Friday night in a frigid church hall with

Lamingtons for beer. Only the most evangelical of reformed alcoholics wouldn't be looking for some kind of additional incentive. One of my new friends preferred meetings in Prahran because of the shopping possibilities. Another picked the groups that had the best cake, now that she'd switched her allegiance from booze to snacks.

Once I'd finished scanning a meeting for men, I'd scan for women. I didn't have a sponsor yet – nobody to tell me 'NO'. I actually wanted one of these third-party consciences. If only I'd had someone following me around saying 'NO' in years gone by. There was a phase, during my teens, when I tried writing *NO* on one hand in biro and *GO HOME* on the other but, if anything, it seemed to serve as an advert to others and a dare to my internal imp.

At each meeting I'd peruse the supplied list of potential sponsors and their phone numbers, scribbling on it little visual cues so I'd remember who was who. *Red glasses. Betty White hair.* Who had the most exotic-yet-wise-sounding name? I wanted a sponsor who had seen it all and would get the measure of me in an instant: a Patsy from *Ab Fab*, an Anita Pallenberg, or a Carrie Fisher.

It's highly recommended that your sponsor be the same sex as you – at least, if you're heterosexual – so I decided to increase my odds of finding someone fabulous by going to a women's meeting. This meant accepting that I was a woman. I'd always fought hard to avoid that kind of association, ever since it had dawned upon me as a teenager that I had been born onto the losing team. My internal misogynist was positive that a women's meeting would be full of neurotic wittering and macramé, with the odd geyser of premenstrual rage. But then, I'd also come to the slow understanding that a girl who was 'one of the boys' was a lost girl indeed.

The most-established women's meeting I could find was in an expensive suburb. If you're nervous about mingling with people whose bottoms are rockier than yours, you can shop for well-heeled AA meetings just as easily as shopping for a potential root or quality cake. It's not enlightened thinking, not when you're likely to learn more from a diverse population, but I hadn't yet wised up to the idea of not 'othering' other people.

A few women sat outside the community centre and smoked in the gardens beforehand, and I was touched at how warmly they greeted me. I didn't realise they were 'greeters'. That's the idea with AA – you receive but you must also give, by becoming a chairperson, or treasurer, or greeter. Doing service is the only way a system without hierarchy and funding can survive.

Once inside, I headed to the kitchen. When you quit booze, your desire for baked goods rises sharply, thanks to the deprivation of sugar that your body would normally extract from alcohol. Meetings tend to be fuelled by cake and lollies, and today there was additionally a birthday cake. This was for someone's 'sobriety birthday', not their 'bellybutton birthday'. You got a white sobriety chip for your first twenty-four hours sober, silver for your first thirty days, gold for two months, red for three months, yellow for six, green for nine, blue and a piece of cake for a year.

There were around fifty of us in the circle, all ages, with a generous percentage of HR consultants and real-estate agents. Some ladies pulled knitting out of their handbags to multi-task. Others arranged candles and boxes of tissues in the centre. In turn, we introduced ourselves and were welcomed, in the rhythmical fashion seen in countless films: 'I'm Mary-Anne and I'm an alcoholic.' 'Hello, Mary-Anne!'

The chairwoman called out significant anniversaries, and the cake was presented as we all sang happy birthday to one woman. This version finished with the chant 'Keep coming back ... *sober*!'

As fresh blood, I was invited to take a silver chip with the serenity prayer stamped on it. 'Not to embarrass you,' intoned the chairwoman, reading from the suggested meeting format, 'but so that we could get to know you better, would those in your first thirty days let us know who you are?'

Mimicking those who had gone before me, I gushed that I was feeling very optimistic – although also very humble – and that I was thankful to be in the right place. I turned the coin around and around in my palm. Then I had an image of myself on a mortuary slab, hauled out of a gutter somewhere. I pictured a forensics team going through my purse; what conclusions they would come to upon finding this chip. One of them would lift it to the light and say with a sigh, 'She didn't keep coming back.'

Today, the theme of the meeting was introduced as 'acceptance'. A woman in her early forties put her hand up to speak.

'I was scum,' she said. 'I fantasised about killing people.'

I glanced at the members' kids playing beyond our circle, but they weren't fazed. Karen's voice was so matter-of-fact that I knew she'd told this story before. Everyone kept their faces neutral as she outlined her murderous fantasies, because AA is a program of honesty and non-judgement, although who's to know if anyone's judging?

In women's meetings, there tended to be an emotional domino effect. If the main speaker was feeling murderous, so would the next shares be. If one wept, so would we all. Had I not gone to these meetings, I wouldn't have received the valuable information that women are most in danger of 'busting' when they're premenstrual, but the flipside of that was, if one woman shared in a PMS rage, any of us so aligned would also be triggered.

The next woman shared about the humiliation of having a restraining order taken out against her by her ex and his new partner. She'd had to learn 'acceptance', all right – the judge was insistent. Harassment was a common theme, whether that be making incessant phone calls to someone, or outright stalking. Obsession with the next drink often goes hand-in-hand with obsessive, intrusive thoughts about another person. You're locked in the same sort of dopamine feedback loop.

Another woman, in her late seventies, trumped everything by telling us about burning down a house by falling asleep with a cigarette on Melbourne Cup day. She'd denied it, of course.

There was Charisse, a CEO whose long, boozy business lunches degenerated into her starting drinking at five in the morning, which was when her hangover woke her. Her husband had checked her into rehab when she'd turned up drunk to a baptism. 'I gave back the company car, the petrol allowance, the salary,' she said. 'It was worth it.'

There was Bella, whose brother had died, which she used as an excuse to drink and feel sorry for herself, until it became all about her. She came across as self-assured, fluent and funny, yet when I glanced at her five minutes later she was berating herself under her breath, close to tears.

There was Elizabeth, who would fall over at work functions and be the only person laughing. Her partner left her because he didn't want to be with a drunk. 'I thought we were having fun,' she lamented.

There was Mary, who had a DUI court case dangling over her like a noose she might have to step into, and who apologised for weeping.

There was Yoshi, a preppy-looking Japanese girl with neatly folded hands and an expensive sweater. Yoshi came to rehab to prove to the fiancé who had left her that she was worth coming back for and wouldn't attempt suicide again. He didn't, but she kept on attending.

And there was Siobhan, who had cheated on her boyfriend and had later been raped by a stranger while they holidayed overseas. She took that to be her punishment.

Bettina put up her hand to speak next, and I noticed a frisson of judgement from the crowd. Bettina was impeccably groomed, with the fragility of a faded 1960s starlet. Her smiles were fleeting reactions, as though her mouth was obeying some internal prompt and then falling slack again. She spoke of her four children, and the way they had all abandoned her when her marriage to their father fell apart. She was barely an adult herself when she married him, she kept reiterating. I recognised what was a familiar narrative thread running through these shares: that of the lonely, rejected child. 'She's spiritually sick,'

Bettina was saying of her sister. 'I pray for her.'

Across the circle, I saw a woman roll her eyes. I consulted my list. Sylvia. She had a slash of red lipstick and a pashmina wrapped around her shoulders. She steadied her face, but it was too late – I'd seen her. I'd found my sponsor.

Lots of women rolled their eyes at meetings – not in judgement, like Sylvia, but like frightened horses. They grasped your hands after the hour had wrapped and beseeched: 'It works if you work it, so work it, you're worth it.' Anxiety is rife among the undrunk. I was the same. I felt like a can of soda that had been shaken up. Sometimes I toyed with the idea of concussing myself as a way of taking the edge off.

A word from my sponsor: You did tell me you picked me because I was the only one without crazy eyes. But the first time I went to a meeting I felt a real benevolence in the room. After I shared, someone came up to me and hugged me. I remember thinking it was the first hug I'd had from a woman in years.

'You're exactly like me,' a woman might assure me, clutching my arm. 'You're my family.' This 'we're all in this together' notion didn't bring out the best in me, but then one of the reminders at AA is not to worry about whether you're 'more than' or 'less than' everyone else and to focus on the similarities, not the differences. They've thought of everything.

Anyway, I wanted to be judged, understood, and then to be fixed. So Sylvia it was.

Sylvia was horribly judgemental. On the grounds of AA being a program of honesty, she seemed hell-bent on brutally pointing out my flaws, or 'character defects', as they're called. I had to wonder if she was projecting, half the time.

'I think you're being a bit self-righteous,' she'd say with a wry chuckle. 'No, not "right" – but "righteous".'

A word from my sponsor: It was obvious to everyone else that I was judgemental and self-righteous, but I couldn't see it. All I could see was those others who were. They weren't matching up to my expectations, and I pointed this out to them regularly. I didn't have a lot of friends then. Once I understood the problem I could work on it and that is what AA helps me do. I still have these character defects, as you are well aware of from when you caught me rolling my eyes. They may have lessened over time, but I am aware of them and can choose to do something about them or not.

I rang up Sylvia and asked for a date, feeling like a thirteen-year-old boy. We met at a gallery cafe – no low-rent hook-ups for us. She opened proceedings by casting a furtive look around the room, flipping open a copy of *The Big Book* and reading in a low, fast voice: '*Rarely have we seen a person fail who has not thoroughly followed our path. Those who do not recover are people who cannot or will not completely give themselves to this simple program, usually men and women who are constitutionally incapable of being honest with themselves.*'

We were about to start my journey through the twelve steps. I was confident I'd be able to gallop through them really fast.

Sylvia made a scoffing noise. 'You never stop going through them. Once you've finished all twelve, you cycle through ten, eleven and twelve on a daily basis. They become a way of life.'

Was there no foreseeable end to AA? First I'd found out that membership was for life, not just till things blew over; now the homework was going to be eternal. For a bit of light relief, I told Sylvia about a man I'd been perving on in the mixed groups. I just wanted to hear myself talk about him.

'Watch out for the men!' she barked, as a waiter slid a double espresso in front of her. 'Whereas female alcoholics are often promiscuous, men are often impotent ... so when they sober up they realise they've got a dick again. Women were always at it, of course. There's a reason they call gin the leg-opener.'

Sylvia explained that when a person first starts to drink or use heavily, they become emotionally stunted, as though fossilised in amber. It's only when they quit that they are able to progress through the ordinary stages of development that they've hitherto managed to dodge.

In case I had any panic about ceasing to be a thirteen-year-old nubile, Sylvia sought to reassure me: 'You won't need Botox. You'll find that when The Promises start coming true your natural expression will be a smile.'

Our hour was up, and Sylvia left me some homework. I read step one as I walked back to the office, confident I could knock this stuff out as quickly as an article. *We admitted we were powerless over alcohol – that our lives had become unmanageable.* Okay. Done.

Speed-reading the book, I could see some of these twelve steps were clearly filler. I would have capped them at four.

There was zero sexual tension for me at these women's meetings, which was good. I didn't have to arrange myself fetchingly or wonder what my hair was doing. In a mixed group, even when every man was a 'nope', there was always sexual tension.

The other problem was speaking up in front of men – as if public speaking, humanity's number-one phobia, wasn't bad enough. (AA is basically toastmasters for booze hounds.) Certainly, in my family, we didn't do personal soliloquies, but I spoke even less in front of my father, who packs a photographic memory of inarguable stats and dates, and has a mind like a steel trap.

Mixed-group shares just aren't very compatible. Women's histories are known as 'baggage', so we do not feel encouraged to burden men with them; besides which, some women have been actively encouraged not to speak up in their private lives. As a result, women's shares – particularly in the company of men – tend to be more scattered. We speak vaguely of our emotions and frustrations. We're agitated and apologetic. We trail off and peter out with a gasp.

A word from my sponsor: Not so. Not for my age group, anyway. I'm not out to impress anyone and don't view AA as a meat market. Maybe this is more about you and your relationship with men.

By contrast, men often spread out, hold court, or lecture, playing it for laughs or effect as they stretch out an arm across the back of the chair next to them. They speak of 'brain snaps' they had when imbibing and they catalogue their drinking milestones.

Younger guys might indulge in one-upmanship; some old-timers boom slogans, sermonise, and thump the table, if there's one handy.

Not every woman fails to flourish in this environment, but the fact remains that Alcoholics Anonymous was originally designed for men. In *The Big Book* – that two-inch thick, hardback bible that every newcomer starts their education with – there's a chapter entitled 'To Wives'. Here's a taster: 'Try not to condemn your alcoholic husband, no matter what he says or does. He is just another very sick, unreasonable person. Treat him, when you can, as though he had pneumonia. When he angers you, remember that he is very ill ... The slightest sign of fear or intolerance may lessen your husband's chance of recovery.'

That chapter's a hangover from the original 1939 edition of *The Big Book*, the first third of which has been left intact in later editions. The book does acknowledge that women can attend AA, too, but it doesn't mention that one of the first women – who joined a group in Akron, Ohio – was hounded out by the local wives, who didn't want her in their homes. It was hard enough, for those wives, admitting that their husbands had this peculiar new life with peculiar new friends that sucked up all their attention, without peculiar new women (probably D.I.V.O.R.C.E.D.) thrown into the equation, too.

When women did start inhabiting 'the rooms' more regularly, they were segregated to one side. Probably, it was thought of as for the best – one ancient AA adage has it: 'Under every skirt there's a slip.' In more recent years, now that there's no segregation in meetings, the art of seducing a newcomer has been dubbed 'thirteenth stepping'.

One alternative to AA in the US is the un-fun-sounding Women for Sobriety (WFS). It's a counter-organisation that rose up in 1975 after its founder, Dr Jean Kirkpatrick, felt that AA wasn't teaching her anything about herself. Instead of twelve steps, there are thirteen acceptance statements in its 'New Life' program. Whereas AA has an emphasis on deflating the ego in order to become humble and abler to surrender to a higher power, WFS argues that women need to focus on developing autonomy. They need to discover a newfound strength in themselves.

I certainly didn't feel like being humble. Perhaps that came down to the AA adage that an alcoholic has 'low self-esteem and a big ego' (which explained my general vibe as editor of the music magazine), but surely the one good thing about hitting rock bottom is that the only way is up? For me, that meant dropping into a share a few mentions of my latest book launch or an after-party, to reinforce my status in society. I would have hated for anyone to assume my life revolved around these church-hall shindigs.

'The other day I accidentally asked for an AA pass instead of an AAA pass,' I might chortle, hoping one of the members would pick up on my ability to procure access-all-areas laminates.

'You should stop that,' advised Sylvia. 'It's wise not to get too specific. Or to show off.'

As I lived out in the country, quite often I'd stay at Sylvia's house after a meeting. It was awkward, sleeping in her adult daughter's old room. I felt like a slovenly interloper who had dibs on her mum. I imagined the sheets would be ripped from the bed the moment I left. And then there was my own mum. Would she feel she had been usurped?

Sylvia's husband, Gino, was a gregarious Italian man who would cook us pasta as their poodles yapped around his feet. He couldn't understand why Sylvia had to keep going to these meetings – now that she was okay – but he tolerated it well enough.

Sylvia and I would sit at the kitchen table and go over my homework. Having raced through the first three filler steps, we were up to step four: making *a searching and fearless moral inventory of ourselves.* I was to list my character defects, chosen from a worksheet. They began:

Arrogance
Attention-seeking
Belligerence
Braggart
Cruelty
Criticalness

'Braggart' didn't even make sense. It was a concrete noun, not an abstract noun.

I wasn't comfortable with this sort of stuff. As far as I was concerned, all of my behaviour over the past twenty years came down to cause and effect, and I didn't think it was right that I should cop the blame. Neither did my psychologist. But in AA you were supposed to tidy your side of the street and not be concerned about someone else's. Over time I came to view that as a positive ploy – otherwise you can waste a lifetime waiting for someone else to change.

One evening I arrived early at Sylvia's house. We were going to do some outreach work at a men's shelter that specialised in drink and drug problems. Often, the residents used it as a place to sleep rather than somewhere at which to turn their lives around; but as long as they didn't bring in drink and drugs, they might be admitted.

I didn't feel comfortable giving them a speech about the dogma of AA when I couldn't relate to the central concept of a higher power. I also disliked that members had to declare a 'bust' and then start from scratch. At many groups, members reveal in turn their number of days or years sober, and someone who has slipped up would have to return to 'I'm one day sober', as if all their hard work had counted for nothing. When pride is one of the few rewards of early recovery, I felt that having it stripped might sometimes prove fatal, or at least send someone on a fatalistic bender.

I lay in Sylvia's bath, observing the churning of my guts, the racing of my heart, the weakness of my chi. 'I think I'm coming down with something,' I called through the door. 'I am. I feel really ill.'

Sylvia called back that I had twenty minutes to get dried and dressed.

'I feel like I'd be really predictable if I cancelled,' I said regretfully, 'but …'

'You would be,' she answered crisply. 'And it's not about you.'

By the time I'd been loaded into the car, I was plagued with further symptoms. A storm loomed outside, adding to the feeling of stifling in my own skin. Human biometeorology studies have shown that admissions to psychiatric units sharply increase with dramatic changes in meteorological stimuli such as atmospheric pressure and wind direction. Personally, I always feel as though the world is ending.

Gino dropped us off at the shelter, where we were met by cheerful night staff. Huddled around the hot-water urn in the kitchen were tonight's other special guests from AA. I felt like a dutiful harbinger of doom.

Once we had been ushered into the TV room, one resident found chairs while another grudgingly pressed mute. Most men averted their eyes as my sponsor spoke of the fruits of sobriety, preferring to stare at the paused image on the TV screen.

When it came to my turn, my voice vibrated like a freshly twanged nerve, which elicited a few curious glances. It shook traitorously as I detailed the hypnosis, doctors, psychiatrists, and hopelessness of my last six months' drinking. Resolutely, I got to my point and planted my flag at the summit.

As I took my seat, the men clapped kindly and murmured, 'Onya.'

The storm in me lifted. It was laughable, how bad an advert I was for the cause. But kudos to them, nobody laughed.

Come gather around, freshly minted sisters of sobriety, because what I have to say may actually save your life.

Every newly sober person has the rude shock of no longer having a buffer against the world; men, as well. If you thought you were a bit nuts before, now you're nuts with the volume turned up. But for many females, there's an extra element at play.

In chapter nine I examined the hormonal mayhem exacted upon the body by substance use. What do you think happens to your body if you quit substances? You might expect that, upon ceasing any chemical tinkering with your mood, liver, guts etc., normal order is restored. Wrong, wrong, wrong! The period of restoring to your factory settings is different for everybody, but much longer than I had anticipated. In the interim, the body's effort to rebalance can have you swinging like Michael Bublé.

A few months after quitting alcohol, I started to get violent mood swings not only around PMT time but around ovulation time. I'm talking two-day crying jags, screaming fits, rampant paranoia, and the inability to string a sentence together. I had no tools to control this frustration anymore. Something as mildly vexing as a toffee-paper rustler on a train or an internet page that took more than a few seconds to load was triggering thermonuclear reactions.

After weeping like a leaky faucet for three days over nothing at all (except, okay, the death of my former life), I dragged myself to my sponsor's house and sat at her kitchen bench, waving one hand ineffectually at my face. I was Alice in Wonderland, all at odds with her new body and shedding enough gallons of tears to drown herself. Only, there was no 'drink me' bottle to fix it.

Panic was always only an irregular heartbeat away. Having an overwhelming day now meant getting fogged in a cloud of white-noise confusion. After a few outbursts at work I was worried about even leaving the house. Maybe this was what it was like to have postnatal depression, I thought, in that it's the one time you most desperately want to have your shit together, but your shit has other ideas.

My doctor tried me on a conga-line of birth control pills. My body furiously rejected them all. I was bleeding all month round, getting pigmentation marks on my face and shoulders, and breaking out in rashes.

Many a late night was spent on a Google odyssey, dropping in combinations of 'PMT twice a month', 'alcohol', 'quitting', and 'fucking hell' into the search box. Eventually I read that alcohol raises estrogen levels, which can contribute to panic attacks, poor memory, anxiety and depression. In one study, blood and urine estrogen levels increased up to thirty-two per cent in women who drank just two drinks a day. By that logic, to remove alcohol abruptly could surely cause an imbalance. Particularly with someone like me, who started drinking around her first period.

But there's no literature for the laywoman on this matter; only scientific papers that take some unearthing and decoding. GPs are generally not au fait with substance use and hormone imbalance either. My doctor, stumped, had sent me for a pelvic ultrasound, with no joy. One of my new mates at AA revealed she was sent for a CAT scan.

It was at this point that AA became really, really useful to me. Where else – except, perhaps, rehab – would I have been able to compare notes with women who were experiencing these things in tandem? Women's meetings are a refuge for ladies in the throes: you can simply flap your hand in front of your face, mid-weep, and explain you have PMS, and everyone understands.

As we sat in huddles over post-meeting coffee, it emerged that many of us had similarly been getting the wrong end of the stick, sending furious emails, making dramatic phone calls, getting suicidal. It was in that premenstrual week of the month that one woman confessed she had to fight the urge to throw herself under a truck if she ventured out to the shops for PMS lollies.

Further conversation revealed that it was always in that one predictable week that those of our number who had 'bust' – i.e started drinking again – had done so. Invariably, it had taken each woman a good year to notice this pattern. Premenstrual tension can make someone in recovery more vulnerable to lapsing – with some rehabs even warning clients to be mindful of their time of month. The anxiety and depression that premenstrual tension can bring, for instance, can trigger distressing memories or self-defeating thoughts.

Why is this not in *The Big Book*? In fact, why isn't this hanging from one of those scrolls when you walk through the door of a meeting? They tell you not to get hungry, angry, lonely, or tired; they don't tell you to download the iPeriod app so you can give advance warning to the world you're about to lose your mind.

Eventually my doctor sent me to a specialist who diagnosed me as having estrogen dominance – a bitter pill to swallow for a woman so determined not to be defined by her sex. It's not an uncommon condition as women get older, but my symptoms were then exacerbated when I abruptly quit alcohol and further upset the equilibrium.

Estrogen dominance can be provoked by too much alcohol, drugs, or environmental toxins, which all impede the liver in eliminating estrogen from the blood. This imbalance would have been worsening in me over time, but in the general mayhem of being drunk and hungover I had mistaken irrational meltdowns for just being part of the magical cycle of a bender.

I've still got the estrogen dominance, but not the post-quitting hormonal maelstrom. It took twelve to eighteen months for my body to calm down and find its new balance. These days, I'm so in tune with it that I'm one of those freaks who can pin-point the exact moment of ovulation.

One time at a women's meeting, a bloke in a suit clomped down the stairs as we gathered ourselves. 'This is a women's meeting,' a small chorus trilled before I even got to see his face.

'Up yours,' he said as his legs retreated.

Mel was first to speak that day. I'd caught myself staring at her quite a lot. She was unspeakably glamorous and self-assured; very film noir. I couldn't imagine what was possibly wrong with her.

As Mel started, her face crumpled. 'I thought I was shit hot,' she said. 'I had everything sorted. My career, my boyfriend, my house.'

Just as I'd thought.

She drew her legs up on her seat and buried her chin into her knees. It was in that house, with all its mod cons, that Mel was brutally raped by her ex-boyfriend one night. The court case that ensued was long, bloody and very public. It triggered all her memories of being sexually abused as a child. Mel listed all the forms of abuse she'd suffered – physical, emotional, sexual – in an offhand, vaguely irritated way. They were labels, but they'd come to be her identity. And they were the quickest way of getting the message across.

As she cried, several women got up and walked out. For the rest of us, the domino effect was in full force.

'Being an alcoholic woman, of course I was raped,' one woman said.

'I let my sister be raped,' said another.

'My best friend died of a backstreet abortion.'

'My mother killed herself.'

Afterwards, when some of us went for coffee and more cake at a nearby cafe, the women who had left earlier were already there. One observed over a latte that this was exactly why she preferred mixed meetings: they didn't turn out heavy. Another explained that she didn't feel we should have to hear stories like that there.

'Where *should* you hear them, then?' I thought.

Upon reflection, it's not that AA's peer system fails women. It's just that professional counselling should probably be an adjunct, which is certainly not discouraged. Trauma can be triggering for other people, and sponsors aren't equipped to deal with it, nor should they be. ('I don't want to hear about your childhood,' Sylvia told me firmly.) They're there to walk a sponsee through the steps and can only pass on their own experiences.

A word from my sponsor: Just remember that psychiatrists probably don't walk the same path as you, whereas in meetings people will come up to you afterwards and say, 'I had that experience, too.' Women can share their raw stories in a gentle way in meetings, and there's a genuine sense of well-meaning. I still go three times a week, and it alters my attitude. I feel cleansed.

In their favour, the women's meetings do tend to employ the holistic approach that drug and alcohol professionals I've interviewed in this book are calling out for in treatment programs. There are annual country retreats that offer meditation and craft sessions, and books of daily reflections for women. These flowery self-care methods are jarring for someone like me, who pinballed aggressively from sexual encounter to confrontation; in fact, they were too jarring for me to get on board. But they're there.

> **A word from my sponsor:** I bought you that book of daily reflections, you ungrateful wretch.

I'd recommend AA or NA to someone who has just quit. There's guaranteed to be a selection of meetings nearby for instant contact with peers in the same boat. They're all free, except for perhaps a gold-coin donation to cover expenses, and there'll be a cross-section of people in recovery to learn from – ranging from those whose families gave up on them, to people who were troubled by their reliance on three glasses of wine a night. It provides the social connection that journalist Johann Hari has claimed, in his book *Chasing the Scream*, is the opposite of addiction – a concept that has gone viral through sharing of related articles on the internet. Its system of twelve steps provides goals that give reward-sensitive people those much-desired surges of dopamine they once received through the pursuit of getting wasted. Additionally, the steps work in a neuroadaptive way, encouraging new patterns of behaviour to rewrite the old, unhealthy pathways through the brain.

I've kept in close contact with the friends I made there, including my sponsor, who lavished me with her generosity and hospitality for a year and a half. I can call them and be instantly understood. In fact, how would I have done without these women in the first year? They were there to answer every question with patience and some gallows humour. Questions such as: How do I make friends with someone now we can't both wet our knickers laughing down the pub? How do I go out to dinner without drinking? How do I have sex sober?

It should be noted that female peer support can also be found elsewhere. Website *Soberistas* has a chat room and forum, along with many articles and blogs. The US-based Women for Sobriety has a chat room (and is amenable to Australian women starting their own meetings); Club Soda holds regular socials in the UK, including the monthly Queers Without Beers. As for the tenets of AA, SMART Recovery has a similar peer-led structure (including a women-only option) without the cornerstone of the higher power or any other kind of spiritual references. There are also online meetings. US-based addiction and recovery website *The Fix* has become heavily weighted towards the female experience.

Australian venture *Hello Sunday Morning* enrols people wanting to quit or cut back on alcohol in an online CBT-based program, and seventy per cent of users are women. Participants can choose their own goals and – on the Daybreak app in particular – are linked into a community of peers, receiving support through Facebook-style 'likes' (though in this case they're 'hugs', 'cheers', a 'stoked for you', a 'here for you', or a comment).

Founder Chris Raine and his team are trialling hundreds of Reddit-style subgroups to see if people flourish more in like-minded communities, be they controlled-drinking groups, strictly abstinent groups, or all-female groups. With the latter, if I posted 'Quitting again today', other women might get a notification on their phone: 'Support Jenny in doing this.' It's not that *Hello Sunday Morning* has a desire to segregate the sexes; it's just interested in using the data to figure out what makes a community effective. 'How do you find the right balance between solidarity and diversity?' ponders Raine. 'We don't want to be led by ideology.'

Something he'll freely admit to having learned from AA is the way the fellowship builds community. 'They've nailed it. They've built an exceptional infrastructure, which is what public health organisations often miss. Those organisations come to us and say, "How do we build what *Hello Sunday Morning* have done, but for gambling?" but they can't conceptually get their head around communities leading themselves.'

Raine thinks that there's a need for innovation within the field of alcohol and drug treatment, maintenance and community. 'If you think about our sector, nothing global has really been created since 1932. AA has an assumed membership of two million people, and there's this assumption of that organisation as being ubiquitous; but compared to the number of people who drink problematically, two million is a tiny drop in the ocean.' He's right. According to a 2001–02 survey of 43,000 Americans by the National Institute of Alcohol Abuse and Alcoholism, seventy-five per cent of individuals who overcome alcohol dependence do so without going to AA or rehab.

'One thing I would change is the ideology of twelve steps,' Raine continues. 'I would remove a generic list of what people need to do and have more of a personalised approach of what they want out of it and then match them with a community that has similar desires and wishes.'

I was skirting the edges of AA, not yet committing to service and putting back in what I was taking out. At the eighteen-month mark, a member told me I was spiritually sick and never going to get better, which I seized upon as the last straw and quit. Feeling like a rebellious child, I had two lines of coke to celebrate, loosening my rule of 'sobriety' to mean 'not drinking', which was my original intention. I didn't make a habit of it.

I'm not the ideal candidate for AA. I'm a sociophobe, a bit stuck-up. I prefer one intense connection to a group situation, which has a tendency to make me switch off. But I've watched people flourish in the nurturing environment of women's groups. My AA friends with professionally enquiring minds – a documentary maker and a journalist among them – sometimes find it hard to suspend their disbelief about some parts of the program. They figure out a way around it. It works for them.

14

KEEPING MUM

When addiction infiltrates the family home

I'm lucky. While *Woman of Substances* isn't exactly a beach read, my experiences only skirt the edges of awful possibility. With my drug use I was just a tourist, albeit the type that overstays their visa. I didn't get into trouble with the police. I didn't drive under the influence, nor even learn to drive. I didn't overdose or take drugs with anyone who did. I didn't get rushed to hospital. Nobody beat me up. I didn't need to have sex with anyone for drugs, nor for drug debts. I didn't want kids, so I didn't accidentally drink through my first trimester, or use throughout a pregnancy. I had a secure childhood and parents who were able to look after me. I haven't seen true darkness and despair. One might even mutter that I didn't try hard enough.

For women whose experiences of addiction infiltrate their family life, whether through domestic violence or impacting on the care of children, the story can become far more complicated. The biggest roadblock is stigma. Stigma deters a mother from seeking help until things are truly dire for her and her children.

Stigma skews the way she is viewed by her family and even by the medical professionals she comes into contact with. The frustrating thing is, stigma makes no sense in a country that has had a national drug policy based around harm-minimisation since 1985. But stigma is generated, daily, by the dominant media, and the dominant media does not buy into harm-minimisation one little bit.

When women make tabloid headlines for serious drug incidents, three key female tropes rise out of the quagmire. The Party Girl overdoses on ecstasy – her first-ever pill, as someone will vouch – and it is fetishised on the front page. The Fallen Middle-Classer is a tall poppy to be scythed, and has been a hit with readers ever since pulp fiction novels depicted nice girls corrupted by jazz dope fiends. But it's the final trope, the Slovenly Mother, who is a dumping ground for disgust.

If a woman is part of a couple who stands accused of parental negligence while inebriated, it will be the mother's Facebook page that the tabloids raid for photographs, and her role that is scrutinised. One example among scores that were published during the writing of this book concerned the triple murder of Adeline Yvette Rigney-Wilson and her kids: *Children murdered in SA went hungry as slain mother put ice habit ahead of her family.* The more appropriate summary, noted journalist Jane Gilmore, in a blog about misogynistic headlines, would have been: *Man murders woman and children.*

Yet if you're a female parent who uses substances, including alcohol, rest assured you're not alone. Stats from *Hello Sunday Morning*'s Daybreak app reveal that fifty per cent of female participants normally drink after work, and fifty per cent of those have kids. In fact, after-work drinking (with an average age of forty) was over two-and-a-half times more likely to be identified as an issue than weekend binging (average age thirty-three).

Mothers do experience additional challenges around substance use. Drinking and driving becomes harder to avoid when kids need picking up and dropping off, particularly in the case of single parents. Stay-at-home mums who feel trapped, isolated, or bored are more at risk of starting their evening wine increasingly early. Mothers tend to be more secretive about their drink and drug use, which also means they're less likely to seek help from their GP – or elsewhere – until the situation has become too severe to ignore. They might additionally have progressed to using both downers and uppers, respectively, in order to get enough rest and then enough energy again. There's also the personal catch-22 that using drugs as a parent is likely to induce shame. And if there were ever a more motivating emotion behind substance use than shame, I'm yet to hear about it.

The children of a dysfunctional parent, such as one abusing substances, tend to take on different mantels. You may fall into one of these roles yourself, but even if you don't you'll recognise them. The Hero is a responsible and over-stressed high-achiever who allows the family to conclude they must not be so dysfunctional after all if they produced this kid. The Enabler is an inwardly resentful peacemaker who seeks to reduce tension by avoiding home truths and maintaining the status quo. The Joker provides relief from tension. The Lost Child disappears into fantasy, chat rooms and books, and eventually might pull away from the family altogether. The Scapegoat takes the focus off the real problems with their problematic behaviour but is actually unconsciously acting out the existing conflict.

No parent wants their kids to grow up in a dysfunctional environment but, in those cases where substance use has slipped from occasional to chaotic, there are some barriers to treatment that mothers, in particular, encounter. Inpatient treatment such as residential detox means finding a child carer. In severe cases, the woman's entire support network may also be using, or in other ways be unsafe around kids. Outpatient treatment requires single mothers to schedule day care around appointments. Government-funded treatment has particularly long waiting lists for mother-and-baby units, while private treatment is unaffordable to many. A woman who has experienced trauma might not be able to find a female-only service; a young or socioeconomically disadvantaged mother might be unable to travel to a service. In some cultures, the idea of a woman admitting to substance use and seeking treatment full stop would be completely unacceptable.

Sometimes the partner will want to continue using, or is a dealer, and the woman might additionally be the victim of domestic violence (quite frequently the baton of that abuse will even be passed from her partner to her son), or financially dependent. Even in milder cases, it's not uncommon for a partner to want the woman to stay put. Dr Jennifer Johnston, a research fellow at the University Centre for Rural Health in Lismore, tells me, 'One woman I interviewed was a stay-at-home mum. Her husband hated her drinking but didn't want her to take the time out to do something about it because it inconvenienced him in having to look after the kids. She had a real struggle to make the space to do a seven-day detox. It was her one shot at getting it right, which is probably not going to be enough.'

Dr Nadine Ezard, clinical director of St Vincent's Alcohol and Drug Service in Sydney, has told me that barriers to treatment are more nuanced than simply lack of childcare. Women often don't seek treatment because they have a perception of what a good or normal woman is: she is a supportive partner, a mother, an earner with a legitimate income. So even women who have already lost their children – or don't have them – can be reluctant to seek help on the grounds that they are not deserving enough, whereas it's seen as a normal part of male development to take drugs and to feel entitled to being heard.

A huge barrier, of course, is fear of repercussion from child protection services, even though most treatment facilities would advocate strongly for a mother. This is particularly poignant for Aboriginal women for whom the idea of children being taken away is so historically entrenched as to be scored into their psyches. Anni Hine Moana, who teaches at La Trobe University in the School of Psychology and Public Health and is a qualified psychotherapist, tells me, 'The really sad thing is, despite the Royal Commissions and the Bringing Them Home report, children are being removed at an even greater rate now. Some of it may have a link to alcohol and other drug use but, in many states in Australia, Aboriginals' rights are being really eradicated, like with the Northern Territory Intervention. Certainly if you are

Aboriginal you've got a greater chance of having your children taken away from you.'

An extra complication of children being removed is that Centrelink payments are reduced, which can mean that a woman is unable to pay rent and is evicted. This then makes it difficult to access appropriate housing in order get her kids back – an awful cycle of despair.

It's a tricky one. In some states, if staff at non-profit treatment services suspects a child could be exposed to parental drug use, reporting is mandatory. In others, reporting is mandatory for doctors, nurses, teachers and police, while non-profits tend to have their own policies and procedures. For instance, the policy of Holyoake, which provides drug and alcohol counselling and support services in Perth, is that the client needs to be safe and encouraged to self-report. That way, the client–counsellor relationship is preserved and the client doesn't feel disempowered. However, staff do report if the client is unwilling and the children are at risk.

'We try and work so that it's a collaborative thing, so that the client sees our reports and we talk to them about it,' explains one Holyoake counsellor. 'We can then support them with legal issues and things like that. The parent is usually relieved because they've been trying to manage all of this and are heavily burdened. They can be given that space to look at how their needs can be met and who else can be brought in to support them.'

There are far too few services that can accommodate children with the mother, but those that do offer the best chances for recovery, not only by lessening a mother's distress but by teaching parenting skills. In November 2016, UnitingCare ReGen – a treatment and education agency – launched the purpose-built Mother and Baby Residential Withdrawal Service in Ivanhoe, the first of its kind in Victoria. It had taken five years of liaising with the Department of Health and Human Services to come to fruition, and arose from trying to meet the needs of a woman and her baby in their adult-withdrawal unit back in 2010. It had been clear that a dedicated service was needed.

That woman, Anne, recalls the disaster of first trying mixed-gender rehab. 'It was eighty per cent male. I felt unsafe, and it was near impossible to focus on my treatment. I overheard a guy saying, "How could a mother do that to her kids?" I felt judged as a woman and a failure as a mother.' In a mother-and-baby setting, by contrast, women who seek help for the sake of their children are to be celebrated. For a struggling mother, accessing such a service – whether voluntarily or by decree – can provide an invaluable safety-net of support, often including playgroups (so that kids can learn social skills before starting school), counselling, legal assistance and childcare. They're all tools that provide the window of opportunity that a mum desperately needs in order to address her own issues.

There are also services across Australia that cater to substance-using pregnant women. At Perth's Women and Newborn Drug and Alcohol Service (WANDAS), midwives deliver around 200 babies a year and support new mums in staying healthy themselves. One midwife, Angela O'Connor, told *Western Suburbs Weekly* that the women seeking help were courageous. 'We don't focus on their drug and alcohol use. We focus on giving them high-quality prenatal and postnatal care,' she said. 'We are very protective of the women. There is a huge stigma attached to drug and alcohol use during pregnancy, but no one knows the path these women have been down to get where they are.'

O'Connor added that, even as midwives for the service, she and her colleagues felt that stigma. 'Often people assume that we have a background using drugs and alcohol because we work in this field, but if we were diabetic specialists you wouldn't automatically assume we had a background with diabetes. The message is these women are no different to anyone else and they deserve the best standard of care.'

Since the turn of the millennium, women have found themselves glitter-bombed with inspirational rhetoric. Blogger Gala Darling promotes 'radical self-love'; Rhonda Byrne's update of the law of attraction, *The Secret*, has sold more than nine million copies; Oprah recommends chasing epiphanies with her 'aha! moments'; Elizabeth Gilbert suggests 'big magic' (that's creativity) could be 'the path to the vibrant, fulfilling life you've dreamed of'.

Sometimes we need to be reminded that there are women without options. I have that realisation when I visit Sydney's Guthrie House, where most of the residents are fresh out of prison. All their lives, these women have been bricked in by their circumstances. They can't just get with the glitter.

Example one. You became dependent on heroin because your mother gave you your first shot when you were twelve. She's looking after your daughter while you're in jail because there was nobody else in your extended family whom you could trust more.

Example two. You were born into a family shattered by Stolen Generations policies. Your teenage mother didn't register your birth, so you've never had the identification necessary to make a housing application, open a bank account, or get a Medicare card. In society's eyes you don't exist, so you're entirely reliant on your immediate community – which means you can only ever be as healthy as that community.

These examples are based on regular real-life cases that manager Glenda Milne tells me about as she walks me around the leafy grounds. The roots of Guthrie House come from the efforts of Women's Liberation members in the 1970s, who were so determined to create a refuge that they broke into vacant houses in Glebe and claimed squatters' rights. The Elsie Women's Refuge remains operational to this day, with sister project Guthrie House founded in 1977, originally as the Women's Emergency Shelter and Training Scheme.

Guthrie House is independent, having narrowly avoided the same fate as Elsie, which was taken over by St Vincent de Paul Society in 2014. That year, across New South Wales, forty-four shelters for women, Indigenous populations and young people were put under new management, with a revised agenda of providing homeless services rather than specialist support.

Milne is a former parole officer, and has retained the habit of keeping a bunch of keys on her belt. I immediately enjoy her off-kilter humour and bracing manner. She's a clear advocate for the women who come through the doors and a believer in going beyond box-ticking. One Christmas, for instance, a woman whose mental health was on the decline was driven 400 kilometres for a family visit. In the case of women with no birth certificate, there's an Aboriginal support worker who visits the elders of the woman's mob, to gather the paperwork that proves an individual's identity.

At Guthrie House, most women have spent time in the criminal justice system. The criminogenic profile of women prisoners in Australia is very different from that of men, with at least eighty-five per cent being victims of abuse. Indigenous women generally experience even higher rates of domestic and family violence, and are also more likely to be incarcerated because of the overuse of 'move-on' powers by police. Women detainees are more likely to have used drugs to ease the psychological distress of mental illness and child abuse, and so drugs have a much greater influence on women's pathways into prison than they have for men.

Generally speaking, women are incarcerated with short, fixed sentences for drug offences or minor crimes such as fraud, and it's not uncommon for a woman to deliberately take the rap. One Holyoake counsellor told me, 'I've worked with clients where women have taken the brunt when there have been house raids. They'll say, "It's better that I go inside, because he can't handle it."'

The problem with a fixed sentence of six months, says Milne, is the recipient receives little rehabilitative effort and might be released to homelessness. So while getting referred to a service such as Guthrie House might initially just mean a safe place to sleep for many women, what comes next might be the first kind of support network they've experienced.

With only twelve weeks to work with, it's impossible for the Guthrie team to open every Pandora's box and deal with the monsters within, then send a woman out to lead a fulfilling, drug-free life, independent of all the old contacts and family members. So they work on fostering connection and new interests.

Efforts to break the cycle of parental neglect are made through the Guthrie House psychologist and mental health worker. The desire is usually there, and it's not uncommon for women to build shrines to their kids next to their beds. 'They want to be good for their children,' Milne says. 'They want their children to be proud of them. The big dream isn't always about having the children back in their care – that's too big a bridge to cross – but certainly just to see them.'

One Holyoake counsellor put it to me this way: 'In prison there's a certain amount to worry about. Outside, there's everything. They do their time and they go back out, usually to the same environment they came from, and suddenly they've got to cope with having five to ten kids scattered everywhere. They beat themselves up because they're supposed to be able to look after their children. And they want to.'

It makes sense that anyone who's already in an abusive relationship with a substance is ripe for an abusive relationship with a person. They're already used to constantly moving the goalposts to excuse their own behaviour, and are accustomed to feeling shame at being judged or pitied by others. They're used to keeping secrets and compartmentalising their lives and, if they're part of a heavy-using scene, they're used to aggro and hierarchy.

A partner, even an abusive partner, might be seen as protection and/or a supply source – both useful tools for the committed substance consumer. Sometimes the relationship is little more than a sexual arrangement between dealer and client, but there are also your Bonnie-and-Clyde-go-to-rehab romances: the Amy-and-Blake, Whitney-and-Bobby, Martha-and-George, Burroughs-and-Vollmer train wrecks. Before too long, life's a Bukowski novel of locksmiths, headlocks, bottle-shop runs and public displays of aggression.

I very nearly didn't include Charlie in this book, since I considered relationships like ours to be the norm … but then again, perhaps moving to the other side of the world to get away from someone isn't normal. So I'll wind things back again and revisit the year 2000, and that rockabilly pub scene in chapter ten where pint glasses sailed through the air.

On our first date, Charlie had taken me for cocktails in Soho. He knew everybody at these members-only clubs because he had been so good-looking for so long that it acted as a kind of passport. He was twelve years older than me, but was lean, with a jet-black quiff, olive skin and grey-blue eyes. He was *so* handsome that in the coming months I would sit across from him and sketch him on cocktail napkins, which he didn't mind. He could sing, too: malevolent 1950s songs from broken baritones. *Who you been loving since I've been gone?*

That first night, Charlie had talked about his closest mates, a couple of devilish rogues whom he was dying for me to meet.

'I *know* you'll fancy all my friends,' he said, so gregariously that my interest was piqued. But within a year he was fanning the flames of his cuckolded fantasies, wondering out loud in the pub if I was sleeping with the various menfolk, and even the womenfolk. I was just passing out on people's sofas. Sometimes those people happened to be on the sofa, too, but the last thing I wanted to do when on a bender was hit pause to have sex.

'It's a joke. Why aren't you laughing?' he'd say.

We lived together for two years, getting kicked out of my Islington flat because of our late-night brawls, then moving into a Camden mews house designed by an architect with groovy 1960s detail. It should have been our new start, except that when the removalists came Charlie was out cold on the mattress, which was sodden with piss, forcing us to load up around him. Recently he'd swapped the early starts of tiling for the late nights of unlicensed sex shops that surrounded my workplace, where I was a subeditor for some popular porn mags. He was delighted to no longer be peeling grouting off his skin all the time, but he was now on Soho's own Silk Road of drugs and gambling and he was seemingly powerless to resist. One night he lost a tooth, and never replaced it. Another night, some girl, somewhere, shaved off all his hair.

I was as fascinated by Charlie as I was infuriated. His penchant for self-sabotage was even stronger than mine, meaning every time he was due to take his teenage son out for a day he would go on such a bender the night before that he was impossible to rouse. A cycle of self-flagellation and remorse would follow. Sometimes, in a rage at rent money blown, I spittled insults at his unconscious form, probably the exact oaths of the tyrannical father he both loathed and idolised. Slowly, surely, we were becoming *that* couple – the one everyone discussed.

Remember how I was accused of stealing money from a party by an opportunistic foe? Quick recap: I didn't steal any money. Knowing I was on the verge of leaving him, Charlie manipulated the situation, threatening to bolster the rumours by revealing what I'd told him about thieving from the squat scene years earlier. When he did that anyway, I did leave – and that's when the real threats started. They piled up in my message bank: thick, drunken vows to kick down whichever friend's door I was hiding behind. If he saw me at the pub, he might insert himself between me and whomever I was talking to, until I left. Spotting me in Camden one night, he ran parallel to me on the other side of Kentish Town Road, yelling across threats to lay me out in the middle of it.

One day, he sent me flowers at work. I came back from lunch to find them nestled in my in-tray, on top of the slides of naked ladies. *I forgive you*, the card read. The same afternoon my mum happened to ring, and I could hide the severity of the situation no longer. My dad came and met me hours later, packing a cold chisel and a sheath knife. Charlie didn't show.

With no children, and no financial or drug dependence on Charlie, I was free to move away. I'd had a job offer from an old friend in Australia. It was at a cafe, not a magazine, but I put my career on ice and took it: the first of what would be two geographicals to Australia. On my journey to Heathrow Airport, I watched Charlie's messages accumulate in my phone, then threw it away in the terminal. It took a year pacing the streets of Sydney to lose the spectre of him. And I've never seen him since.

The role that drugs and alcohol play in domestic violence – cause or tool – is hotly debated. What is known is that in the 2015–16 financial year in Australia, more than 25,000 suspected family violence offenders were recorded as being possibly or definitely on drugs, while more than 24,000 were down as being possibly or definitely drunk. But as Professor Wayne Hall, who's the director of the Centre for Youth Substance Abuse Research at the University of Queensland, says, 'People usually have a history of violence, either of being on the receiving end as children or inflicting it on others. Alcohol should be regarded as an aggravating factor, but you need to address more than the drinking. You have to change thinking patterns and ways of dealing with conflict.'

There's also a challenge for those on the receiving end. Women will often accept domestic violence as their lot if they perceive themselves to be 'bad' women – such as in the case of using drugs – but never more so than if it is the norm in their community. One Holyoake counsellor told me, 'A lot of clients I see don't even realise they're in a domestic violence relationship, because they quite often get caught up in those sorts of relationships from learned behaviour. If there's a culture of covering up, there's likely to be little recognition of something being a problem in the first place.'

It's funny, what's taboo in a drug-fuelled community and what's not. Heroin was strictly verboten in the squat scene I'd drifted around upon first leaving home. There was only one girl who took it and she was not approved of. I didn't mind her. She once taught me how to put on a full face of makeup using a tube of Smarties. But this same squat community granted amnesty to some members who ought to have been expunged. There was the man from South Africa who regularly beat his painfully thin, always sunny girlfriend; and besides him, random eruptions of violence at which people muttered, but did not act.

I didn't act. I was sitting in the back of a packed car at a festival, where we could spliff-on in peace. The ecstasy I'd taken was strobing my vision unpleasantly, and I was about to turn to my neighbour and enquire as to his own outlook when the man in the driver's seat, a big bastard, suddenly delivered three fast, hard punches to his girlfriend's face. She'd been chatting, that was all. Now she sat trying to stifle her shuddering gasps. I looked across at the others, who had snapped silent, their faces drawn. My friend shook her head almost imperceptibly.

In such a community, there's an unspoken pact: if you are constantly blurring the boundaries to excuse your own behaviour, you must do so for the whole group, letting transgressions slide. The grey area becomes ever wider as ranks close. Women have little currency in these communities, and women out drinking with their children left at home, which elicits disapproval, have barely any protection at all.

Years later, one of my closest friends from that pub scene that Charlie and I hung out at told me that her boyfriend – admittedly, known as King Hit – swore pleasantly over a fancy dinner that he'd kill her if she ever cheated on him. She excused herself, went to the ladies' room and threw up in the sink. From then on she always kept cab fare in her purse in case she needed to run. Despite drinking with her three days a week, I'd had no idea.

What if the worst happens? What if kids are effectively orphaned by their parents' drug use, either through actual death or through abandonment? That's where Jane Rowe steps up – in the state of Victoria, at least.

We should never judge a book by its cover but, with her Anita Pallenberg fringe and her arms ringed to the elbows with bangles, Rowe's cover is virtually embossed with 'Interesting Story'. As a teenager in the early 1970s, she began her career working at Richard Branson's new Virgin Records and immersed herself in the London punk scene. Heroin and speed were the drugs du jour, and many of her peers overdosed or succumbed to hepatitis C because of a lack of basic harm-minimisation knowledge.

Upon moving to Australia, Rowe started volunteering at a St Kilda rehab, Windana, and trained to be a counsellor. In 1998, she founded the Mirabel Foundation, which now supports more than 1500 kids around Victoria who are in kinship care – such as the care of their grandparents – because of parental drug use.

Mirabel's staff of twenty-five includes youth and childcare workers, grief and loss counsellors, social workers and educational workers. Through the foundation's support groups, kinship carers can connect with one another, as well as receive counselling themselves. There are also homework clubs, rural camps, and the capacity for overnight stays in Melbourne. Sadly, the role of Mirabel in a kid's life often needs to be long term.

Back in the 1990s, the main problem Rowe was encountering was heroin. 'Time and time again I was seeing mums needing a bed and overdosing because there wasn't one available, which left these orphaned kids,' she says. Now Australia has the highest rate of methamphetamine consumption of any developed country, which brings with it a very different set of issues. 'What we're getting these days,' says Rowe, 'is a child witnessing a younger sibling being murdered by Mum's mad boyfriend.'

Methamphetamine has become Australia's most affordable and accessible drug. It's easily manufactured, even in built-up areas, so it's purer than a drug such as cocaine that has been imported and cut multiple times along the way. For these reasons, it's expanded into the terrain of other substances and scooped up those consumers. And women are pulling ahead in its usage. Every three years the National Drug Strategy Household Survey provides cross-sectional data on substance use in Australia, and the 2013 results revealed that, among past-year users of methamphetamines, women surpassed men in terms of the most frequent use.

The majority of the meth-using population does not become dependent or experience major problems, but for those who work in the treatment sector, who see the pointy end, its effects are devastating. One Holyoake counsellor explains to me why meth can be an attractive drug to mothers despite its capacity for destruction. 'We're observing family systems and work systems quite different from those we encountered twenty years ago, so the pressures on mums are very different,' she says. 'Many women are using meth to enhance their performance, because they're trying to manage the house, the work, the study. Meth might keep them alert and help them to multi-task, but your thought processes aren't working so well. You forget things. So you might stop using it for a bit, but then you can't cope as well as you used to, and you're tired without it. There's often relapse after relapse.'

To avoid the inevitable carnage, Rowe believes passionately that drug use needs to be a health issue, not a criminal issue. 'There are so many young women who are too frightened to put their hand up because they're worried that their children will be taken,' she reiterates. 'The great thing about medically supervised injecting rooms is that they could also offer some support and make sure the kids are getting health checks. It's all about drawing people in so that other services can support them.'

At the time of writing, Australia's only safe-injecting room (also known as a drug-consumption room or DCR) is in Sydney. Drug reformers advocating for more facilities point out that inhalation rooms for meth consumers are also needed. According to Dr Alex Wodak and Matt Noffs, writing in *The Guardian* in June 2016, 'In many countries, people using a DCR can have a shower, shampoo their hair, and wash and dry their clothes, buy some cheap and nutritious food, talk to a counsellor, see a healthcare worker, see a doctor and get supervised training for a job.'

In the meantime, it's services such as the Mirabel Foundation – locked in a desperate grind of fundraising efforts – that have to pick up the pieces. This, amid unhelpful headlines that further stigmatise and scare off the women who need help earlier. Not long after I meet Rowe, right-wing commentator Miranda Devine received widespread media coverage for her solution of offering ice-dependent parents a sterilisation bonus.

That's not a new idea, of course. From 1907 onwards, until repeals in the 1960s and 1970s, thirty US states passed laws mandating compulsory sterilisation of the mentally deficient, which included alcohol dependence in many states. The Nazis were slower off the mark, with their eugenic treatment of alcoholics, not starting until 1933. Since 1997, an independent venture, Project Prevention, has been offering financial incentives for drug users in the US and UK to pursue sterilisation and long-term contraception. Its founder, Barbara Harris, was quoted in *Marie Claire* UK as saying, 'We don't allow dogs to breed. We spay them. We neuter them. We try to keep them from having unwanted puppies, and yet these women are literally having litters of children.'

When I visit Kamira, a residential drug and alcohol treatment service for women on the Central Coast of New South Wales, a case worker there gives me the lowdown on 'litters' from the point of view of someone at the coalface. She liaises with the state government's Family and Community Services department on a client's behalf, and she'll often find that the client has been involved with the department since birth. 'When faced with their own children being taken away, they suffer grief and loss as well as their drug and alcohol issues,' she says. 'A woman I'm working with now has just seen her case notes and found out about things that happened to her as a three-year-old that she wasn't even aware of. The process of going through the court can be retraumatising. There's trauma on trauma on trauma.'

A way to salve that pain is by having another child. 'Let's say she's in her late twenties and has multiple kids. If they remove the last two, she'll just have two more. She has plenty of time, so how many are going to be removed? It's a small population that this is applicable to, but it's this population of people who will keep failing. Instead we could just get her into treatment with her children.'

Therein lies the rub. The chances of a woman with children being able to find a bed when she needs it are minimal. Take Kamira itself. The current building was purpose-built by the government to have twenty-two beds, yet for years the same government only funded eleven places. That's now risen to sixteen, but it's still dependent on Kamira's funding applications being successful in each three-year cycle. When you further consider that effective treatment tends to last five to seven months, followed by an outpatient after-care stage, it's obvious that more energy needs to be poured into accommodating vulnerable women than into sterilisation plans that demonise lower socioeconomic populations.

Dr Adrian Carter is a neuroethics researcher based at Monash University's Brain and Mental Health Laboratory. He says, 'Programs that provide financial incentive for a medical procedure fail to meet basic medical and social care. They treat women who use drugs as means rather than as respected autonomous members of society. These programs also unfairly target women from lower socioeconomic backgrounds. More affluent women have the resources to access medical and social support that keeps their drug use and behaviour out of sight of the coercive power of the state.'

He adds, 'Given the current situation where many people are unable to access minimal addiction treatment and support, the use of scarce government resources to induce women to undergo long-term contraception is inappropriate.'

Persevering pioneers such as Jane Rowe hear enough success stories to know the eternal fight for funding is worth having. She describes one of the Mirabel children, Heaven Lee, who is now an adult and a regular public speaker for the cause. 'People say to her, "What a beautiful name your mother gave you." She laughs and says, "Actually, my mother named me after her favourite character in a book by the author of *Flowers in the Attic.*"'

Rowe continues, 'We recently went out to dinner and she said, "You know what, I don't think I'm angry with Mum anymore." She's managed to join the dots that her mother suffered from depression and then her self-medication got out of control. It's great when kids make those links, because that's what it's often really about. It's about mental health issues.'

Let's return to Adeline Yvette Rigney-Wilson, the woman of the *Slain mother put ice habit ahead of her family* headline. Very little has been reported about Steven Peet, the partner who murdered her, but Rigney-Wilson was an Aboriginal woman, which means she was thirty-four to eighty times more likely to experience violence than a non-Indigenous Australian.

Writer Celeste Liddle, on her blog *Dead Aboriginal Women*, keeps a grim tally of each year's victims of assault and domestic violence, and is painfully aware of the sort of stigmatising headlines that accompany each story. 'It seems that there is a whole new level of victim blame and demonisation at play when sexism intersects with racism within this country,' Liddle says, writing in *Daily Life* in June 2016.

In one of the only news stories that moved past Rigney-Wilson's methamphetamine use, *The Advertiser*'s Lauren Novak talked to the many carers who had looked after Rigney-Wilson throughout her troubled childhood. We learned that Rigney-Wilson was one of nine siblings. She was shunted around the country as a child, and was frequently around adult drug use. She had a large scar on her scalp and suffered an ear infection so serious that she had to be flown to hospital. It was widely accepted that she had experienced terrible abuse and neglect. One carer said she hoped that Rigney-Wilson's death 'will change practices for women who have been through what she has been through'.

With the huge demand for beds in facilities such as Kamira, Rigney-Wilson would have struggled to find treatment in accommodation with her children. To save herself she would more likely have had to lose them to the care system, to be shunted from pillar to post the way she once was herself.

As is increasingly becoming a catchcry from AOD workers and researchers alike, and which is all too plain here, addiction is *not about the drug.*

15

A CALL TO ARMS

How drug and alcohol research and treatment can fail women

While I was writing this book, three academics I interviewed raised concerns about gender bias in drug and alcohol research. Such bias results in a very male picture of addiction – that is to say, a picture of addiction without the extra complexities that this book has detailed.

Professor Jan Copeland, director of the National Cannabis Prevention and Information Centre, began her career in the 1990s researching and publishing groundbreaking papers about the quality of treatment for women in both single-sex and mixed-sex services. She says she was told by a leading drug and alcohol physician back then that 'it was a complete waste of time to address anything to do with women because men are in the majority and that's where the focus should be'.

Jane Ussher, Professor of Women's Health Psychology at the University of Western Sydney, has a similar story. 'As a junior researcher I was advised by my head of department not to do women's health research, and definitely not anything feminist, because it would completely ruin my career. He told me I should do basic experimental research. He didn't say "on men", but that was the implication.'

Not much has changed. Another academic, who asked to remain anonymous, tells me that currently: 'Gender isn't a big priority on the agenda. It's just like everything else – it's a patriarchal society and that's how the research world operates, too.'

It's also how the treatment world tends to operate because, there, men are still seen to be the norm. It's true that women access addiction treatment at a much lower rate than men, the reasons for which are examined in detail in chapter fourteen. This then means that the data gathered from treatment populations tends to be skewed towards the male experience and, to further complicate matters, many services don't gender-split their own data. Treatment policy thus continues to be one-size-fits-all in many services, despite the fact that the pathways that lead women into addiction, and the traumas that they will likely endure, are very gendered.

Even so, it was nothing short of a bombshell for Australian media when, in October 2016, a report from the National Drug and Alcohol Research Centre at the University of New South Wales concluded that, by the end of the last century, men's and women's drinking rates were actually about equal. Further, there was some evidence that women born after 1981 may be drinking at higher rates or in more harmful ways than men. This was based on pooling data from sixty-eight studies about drinking habits across thirty-six countries with a sample size of more than four million men and women – pretty exhaustive in its reach.

So men are not in the majority. In any case, when it comes to drug and alcohol research, we cannot just go with the majority rule. To illustrate this, I'm going to describe the way that male-biased research backfires on females.

When Melbourne neuroscientist Rachel Hill discovered that, of the 710 scientific studies she had reviewed for her paper on schizophrenia research, seventy-five to eighty per cent had exclusively used male rodents, she immediately recognised the irony.

By rejecting female rodents on the grounds that the many stages of the reproductive cycle would contaminate the data, scientists were ignoring an inconvenient truth. If the fluctuating hormonal levels of a female rat will complicate a pharmacology trial, then the drug being trialled cannot be relied upon to have the intended effect on human females. That's something the manufacturer of sleep aid Ambien was forced to confront when women kept overdosing on the recommended dose, and of course it also applies to drug replacement and maintenance medications.

Females move through major endocrine change in their lives – puberty, pregnancy, menopause – but even just by being at different phases in her monthly cycle, a female could experience different results and side effects from a drug. Then there are the other gender disparities: the way fat is distributed differently in male and female bodies; the difference in metabolising drugs between males and females; and weight differences. If a drug is marketed at a dose that's appropriate for a seventy-kilo male, it could endanger a female.

The director of the Monash Alfred Psychiatry Research Centre, Professor Jayashri Kulkarni is adamant that male data cannot be extrapolated into the female population the way it so frequently is. 'All you need to do is monitor the cycle,' she says in exasperation. 'Yes, it's another variable, but there are statistical ways to do that. You recruit larger numbers and so on. It's not an insurmountable problem, but people use it to say let's not bother.'

Professor Wayne Hall is director of the Centre for Youth Substance Abuse Research at the University of Queensland. He agrees that: 'the lack of gender-specific research is an ongoing problem. The low-hanging fruit for research is to exclude women from trials, and as a consequence we know very little about the effects of drugs on women.'

As Hall explains, ethics committees – be they attached to universities or hospitals – tend to be risk-averse. 'They're typically very nervous about giving drugs to women during her whole reproductive period because of the risk that the woman is pregnant and there could be harm to the fetus.'

Hall recalls a clinical trial of buprenorphine – used as a heroin substitute – in which the sample group actually needed to be pregnant women who were opiate dependent. 'It took forever to get through ethics,' he says, 'and the conditions under which they could recruit were very difficult to achieve.'

Another obstacle faced by researchers is that their project is likely to build on existing studies – perhaps even by the same department – which themselves probably conform to male bias. Additionally, funding is scant and competition fierce. It becomes still more scant if research has to be expanded to cover all genders and ethnic groups.

Funding isn't just a problem in drug and alcohol research. Investment into researching coronary artery disease has been far greater for male studies than female, yet females often show different symptoms and are at greater risk of mortality. In 2005 this inequality triggered a review by the UK Cabinet Office and also prompted the National Heart Foundation of Australia to make vigorous efforts to collate data on females. This same stringency is needed in the drug and alcohol field.

Since 1993 the National Institutes of Health in the US has advised that 'women and minorities' should be included in clinical research (it goes without saying that culturally and linguistically diverse populations are similarly frequently excluded). Professor Hall notes that, even when adequate numbers are included in a sample, the data is often not split separately by sex to observe differences. 'The better way to go about it,' he says, 'would be specific funding for research on these issues, and a call for research proposals to address these particular issues.'

An alternative view comes from Dr Nadine Ezard, who's the clinical director of the Alcohol and Drug Service at St Vincent's Hospital in Sydney. She says there's an argument for *not* separating data, provided the sample group is diverse in the first place. 'When we think of gender in terms of biochemical makeup and hormones, it's a reductionist idea. Your gender role and experience is going to be much more important than what's going on biochemically,' she advises. 'Often trans populations have greater levels of stigma and trauma. We need to move outside of the gender binary, so that it's not just about men and women – there's a quantum spectrum of diversity. Then you can look at the effects on sub-populations if you have enough numbers.'

So that's research. What about treatment? Opinions differ among AOD workers as to whether mixed or gender-specific groups are more advantageous.

Dr Maria Duggan of the Australian Health Policy Collaboration tells me, 'The keys to developing effective services for women lie in understanding and acknowledging the effects of living as a female in a male-dominated society. The influence of male domination is so pervasive that it is unseen. One result is that programs and policies called "gender neutral" actually reinforce the unconscious – and hegemonic – view that the male is the default human.'

In April 2016, Duggan published a paper revealing that forty-three per cent of Australian women have experienced mental illness at some time, with more women than men experiencing symptoms in the previous twelve-month period. This high prevalence is attributed to the totality of women's experiences, including social and economic inequality.

According to Duggan, the kind of issues that might contribute to a woman's dependence on substances – more so than for a man – include shame and stigma; relationship problems; fear of losing children or a partner; lack of services for women, particularly those with children; and physical and sexual abuse. To that I can add post-traumatic stress disorder, which in substance-abusing populations is five times higher than in the general population.

Duggan emphasises the findings of multiple studies over the past few decades about the role that serious traumatic experiences play on women's mental and physical health. Take the ongoing work of California-based clinician Dr Stephanie Covington, who pioneered research into trauma-informed and gender-responsive services. In one of Covington's first studies on addicted women, seventy-four per cent reported sexual abuse, fifty-two per cent reported physical abuse, and seventy-two per cent reported emotional abuse. These kinds of towering statistics have been backed up in countless studies since.

'However, these research insights have not been incorporated into treatment regimens or policy as yet,' Duggan confirms. 'Awareness of gender issues must be part of the clinical perspective.'

Professor Jayashri Kulkarni agrees. 'It's almost as though the trauma side of it has been put in a box and "someone" is dealing with it,' she says. 'We did a survey of whether clinicians working in mental health took a history of trauma in the females admitted to the service. More than half did not. Somebody once said to me, "The social workers are dealing with that."'

She puts on a puzzled voice. 'The social workers are saying, "What?"'

Dr Nadine Ezard reports that it's only recently that research has emerged suggesting it's possible to treat trauma and substance abuse at the same time. She says, of her days at a drug and alcohol service in the 1990s, 'We were told that evidence showed that any attempt to tackle the trauma will make the substance use worse, because the substance use is the coping mechanism. So you didn't address the trauma until the substance abuse was under control. Now we think differently, but there's a need for clinicians who are trained to at least screen, detect and refer for some other issues. Otherwise, you might have someone thinking, "Don't tell me about your trauma because I don't know what to do about it"; or "Don't make me ask about your sexual history. I'm happy to ask anything about where you stick your drugs ..."'

The way forward, suggests Duggan, is to follow the principles of research by Stephanie Covington and her peers when developing women's integrated treatment (WIT). These include acknowledging the impact of gender; developing policies, practices and programs that promote healthy connections to children, family, significant others and the community; additionally, addressing trauma and mental health issues; and providing women with opportunities to improve their socioeconomic conditions. Otherwise, she says, 'nothing will change'.

Important conversations are being had on this front at drug and alcohol conferences in Australia. In 2013, the New South Wales–based Network of Alcohol and Other Drug Agencies (NADA) formed the Women's AOD Services Network and were funded to implement the Women's AOD Services Development Program. These projects have designed a Gender-Responsive Model of Care, a Practice Guide and training aimed at the non-government AOD sector. They have also produced training and policy templates to support those working with women experiencing domestic violence. Leading researchers and clinicians from around the country contribute their findings on topics such as pregnancy, parenting, and family-inclusive practice; gender-responsive treatment; social-anxiety treatment; and the importance of trauma-informed practice.

One interesting approach, which can be worked alongside the more commonplace cognitive behaviour therapy, is compassion-focused therapy. This teaches women how to self-soothe in a healthier way, with therapists working on an emotional, cognitive, physical, behavioural and spiritual level. There's a focus on reconnecting with the body, using soothing exercises such as yoga and meditation, mindfulness and trance states.

Another approach is narrative therapy, which was developed by Australian social worker Michael White and Kiwi therapist–academic David Epston in the early 1980s. It is widely thought to be culturally safe for use in many contexts, including addressing substance-use problems as experienced by Indigenous women, whose underpinning issues of trans-generational and historical trauma may not be addressed by modalities designed by white practitioners. In fact, many narrative practices emerged from partnerships between the early practitioners and Aboriginal community workers, such as Aunty Barbara Wingard and Jane Lester.

Anni Hine Moana, who teaches at La Trobe University in the School of Psychology and Public Health, is undertaking doctoral research in the area of Indigenous women's substance use, and the self-conscious emotion of shame. She tells me that narrative therapy encourages the client to look at some of the dominant narratives that they are using to give themselves a hard time: 'I'm to blame', 'I'm an alcoholic', 'I'm a bad mother', or 'I'm a failure'.

These narratives are deconstructed within the context of the enormous social, historical and sexual violence that the client is likely to have experienced. The therapist and client will then look for the subjugated narratives of resilience, courage and strength, and work on lifting those to the fore.

A key factor of narrative therapy is externalising the problem – the problem is the problem – *never* the person. 'I prefer not to use words like alcoholic or drug addict,' says Hine Moana. 'Our identities are multi-faceted. I am interested in what has happened on a woman's journey through life that has made heavy alcohol or other drug use so attractive to her. What is her story?'

Psychology, Hine Moana says, is helpful, but it often uses a particular cultural lens and can focus on the individual and on changing behaviour. By contrast, narrative ideas look at how politics, history and social contexts affect all aspects of our experiences.

'Through working with women, most of whom have experienced violence in various forms, I have become interested in our experiences of gender and how that may play into substance problems,' Hine Moana says. 'The whole area of women and addiction has been a very neglected area of enquiry. Addiction is a complex issue, and I am suspicious of any one-dimensional explanation for why it occurs.'

How disgusted my younger self would be – that baby misogynist who was defiantly, desperately one of the blokes – to learn that my addiction story makes for a very female case study.

Of course, it starts before I even pick up a drink or a drug, when I'm playing dead in my bed as a seven-year-old – the moment that shame hotwires my brain. And then my treacherous gender continues to define every step into the abyss.

At thirteen: I begin self-soothing with alcohol. Seventeen: I trade sex for drugs, and can only cope with the former by being off my face anyway. Eighteen: I sit in a police station, reporting a rape that had occurred during a blackout. Twenty-two: I chattily admit to a string of GPs that I'm dependent on speed, and they put me on variations of antidepressants even while acknowledging that I'm not depressed. Twenty-seven: I move to another country to escape domestic violence.

When I seek treatment, it suddenly seems as though my gender is irrelevant. The outpatient counsellor gives me useful tools but avoids the subject of trauma. The Alcoholics Anonymous groups I attend refer to 1930s literature that largely excludes the female experience. When my hormonal levels rage in protest at my new-found abstinence, I can find no mention of the phenomenon in any recovery literature, only in scientific research papers.

And then when I interview men for this book about women, a couple of them give me one male case study after another. But, look: men aren't the norm, neither in general population terms, nor in substance-using populations. Pathways into addiction aren't gender-neutral, and neither is mental health. If all this isn't reflected in research, treatment and policy, then a huge chunk of the intended demographic will not receive appropriate support. I dare to hope we can all agree on that.

16

CHOOSE YOUR OWN ADVENTURE

Eight ideas for emancipation your way

My life should have been a Duran Duran video. Exotic climes, open-top Jeeps, gleaming hotel lobbies with marble floors and ceiling fans rotating lazily over potted palms. I should have been thumping hard-oak boardroom tables and powering through airports in my safari suit.

Upon closer examination, though, it was all pubs and piss-stained raves and sitting on the toilet with my head in my hands. Same people, different stupid haircuts. And now even that was over.

The really good news is that quitting is one of those rare transition opportunities we sometimes have thrust upon us (see also: death, divorce, bankruptcy, redundancy, pregnancy, natural disaster). A rip appears in our existence, and we can choose to leap through its flickering portal into an entirely new dimension. Or we can make do.

This chapter is for the quitters and the quitters-in-contemplation. It's time to choose your own adventure.

1. Look for the window of opportunity

When your foot is caught in the hamster wheel of routine, be that a mechanical dependence on painkillers, or a stressful period in which you're only kept afloat by alcohol, it's likely you do not have the headspace required to break free. So this is the time to scan the horizon for opportunity.

Maybe this window will appear because of what less imaginative people would classify as a bad situation: a jail sentence, a seizure, a stretch in hospital, a separation. Alternatively, it might appear because of a chance for a breather. My cigarette intake went up dramatically – from zero – during the writing of this book, in which period I also isolated from friends and ceased all exercise apart from a little beaten track to the espresso machine. It wasn't until I handed in the first draft that I had the mental space to give up the smokes again – and to call at least one friend a day.

Another example: on one trip home to England, since quitting drinking in 2009, in great spirits, I drank with friends. It was unexpected, but uneventful. In fact, I didn't even flog it hard enough for a hangover. Still, by week three I could feel old habits slipping back in – of plotting the next excuse to drink, and of sneaking in doubles at the bar – and with them, a lot of fear. It was hard to find the will to stop while feeling rudderless overseas. I fixed my sights upon my return to Australia – my window – and quit again the moment the plane touched down. For good measure, I locked in some appointments with a psychologist specialising in addiction.

According to neuroscientist Marc Lewis, author of *Memoirs of an Addicted Brain* and himself a former user of heroin (and whatever he could rip off from pharmacies), when it comes to quitting, 'People have to really be ready, because there has to be a powerful surge towards other goals. Goals about their relationships and feeling whole, connected and under control. The striatum is highly activated, ready to pull us towards new goals.'

In other words, simply quitting won't really cut it. There needs to be vision and a desire for greater things; for the 'ideal self', as it's often called in counselling terms. When you feel the world tremble on its axis, shove.

2. Hack your reward system

After the honeymoon period of quitting comes the period of 'maintenance', otherwise known as 'the rest of your life'. During this period of the rest of your life, your mind will be constantly trying to convince you to do impulsive (but hilarious) things that you will regret. From a neuroscientific point of view, this is because it's jonesing for dopamine.

There's a line in *The Big Book* of Alcoholics Anonymous that warns: 'Remember that we deal with alcohol – cunning, baffling, powerful!' But alcohol isn't actually that smart. Try switching 'alcohol' for 'your mind'. Your mind is King Joffrey in *Game of Thrones*: it demands to be entertained or it will pick up its crossbow and splatter your guts. And by quitting whatever you've quit, you've just taken away its favourite plaything.

Life, post-quitting, is an endless game of swapsies. In the first year alone, I cycled through excessive use of energy drinks, coffee, nicotine, Candy Crush (tip: download a game onto your phone immediately, if you urgently need distracting from drinking or using, and fall into its reward vortex), cold-and-flu tablets, an eating disorder, sexting and porn. So much porn. As soon as I noticed one habit had got out of hand and nipped it in the bud, another would rise up in its place. One friend, when she quit drinking, resumed the gambling she'd given up years before. She funnelled the money from the joint account she had with her boyfriend into the pokies every night, telling him she was late because the tram had been delayed. Same behaviour, different outlet.

These are all distractions from facing feelings, but there's probably also something else at play: cross-sensitisation. This phenomenon means you have grown so accustomed to exciting spikes of brain chemicals from your drug of choice that over time you have turbocharged the reactivity of your reward system. Now that you've quit, your brain's feelers are casting about for dopamine-rich vices to keep the revs up.

Does that ever stop? Potentially. Dan Lubman, who is Professor of Addiction Studies and Services at Monash University, told me in an interview for *The Saturday Paper* that, if a person can avoid over-stimulating the reward system for about three months, cravings should wear off as natural enjoyment floods back in. But I have to be honest here, I've found that completely impossible – we're not just talking avoiding booze or meth here; we're also talking nicotine and caffeine.

The idea of being so enslaved bothered me greatly, so six years after quitting drinking I went to see an addiction counsellor. I wanted a second opinion on whether I should really care that I was constantly trying to rodeo-ride my reward pathways. Maybe I should just cut myself some slack.

The counsellor chuckled at this. 'Everyone will always have to be vigilant about aspects of their behaviour,' he said, 'but perhaps particularly you and me.'

He gestured at the ostentatious knick-knacks around his office, the spoils from some extravagant overseas shopping sprees. Compulsive buying is a close relative of problematic substance use, so of course there's the likelihood that they become interchangeable.

The counsellor suggested I go to Narcotics Anonymous meetings – like him. I declined, preferring his view that some kind of vigilance is always required and, sometimes, extra-extra vigilance, at which point I go and see a counsellor again (because if there's one thing I will be really prescriptive about, it's that no matter how self-aware and wise a journeywoman of addiction you consider yourself to be, there are trained professionals you should go and see who know far more than you). That's life, isn't it? Monitoring yourself and keeping yourself in check. There's a temptation to think of people who have never been substance dependent as being 'other' and 'okay' but, believe it or not, they have to keep themselves in check for stuff, too.

And so I continue to juggle my rewards and milk those dopamine-udders, making sure any sole activity doesn't start sprinting for the finish line. I do have some harm-minimisation techniques. I replaced smoking, for instance, with making video diaries to improve my public speaking; and, when I got bored of that, bought a drum kit to have a bash on. If I'm in a social situation I'll just turn everything into a game: *Learn something about this person they never expected to tell you.* If I've been slighted and the hurt feelings demand alcohol, the situation has to be turned into a challenge: *How quickly can you get over this slight?*

In short, I try to reframe everything for my inner King Joffrey so that a loss looks like a win. Specifically, it needs to look like an *immediate* win. We're told that the 'fruits of sobriety' are good health, improved relationships and mental fortitude. Very true, but you can't replace instant gratification (cigarettes, drugs, alcohol) with delayed gratification (wellbeing) and expect your monkey mind not to laugh at you. It's just not an equal trade-off. So know what goals your mind likes best. I wound up doing this to extremes, as you're about to find out.

3. Return to being a sensation-seeker

After quitting, I was no longer in any pressing physical or emotional pain. Instead: the vast expanse of boredom. Cruelly, boredom kicks in just after the belief that you've reinvented the wheel wears off. The novelty of all those firsts – first party sober, first holiday sober, first shag sober – has faded. In its place, taupe eternity. At first, having flatlined feelings is a novelty in itself. No more crying jags! No more thrashed hotel rooms! But then that wears off, too. And if you haven't gauged by now that boredom is a dangerous, dangerous thing for the substance-inclined, I refer you back to chapters three and ten.

Back in 2010, eighteen months after quitting, I decided I urgently needed to come up with a plan, or risk toppling into the boredom abyss. Recently I had dyed my hair a nondescript shade and started dressing more conservatively. I felt as though an era was over, and that era was my life. I was winding down. To reverse that, it felt imperative that I foster my sense of humour and curiosity, both of which I'd lost.

Around that time, I went to the funeral of a friend's father. I'd never met Peter, but the eulogies described an extraordinary man. When the advance of his cancer meant he could no longer sail, he focused on the cello. When that became too difficult, he took up painting. On his deathbed he read a book on quantum physics. His thirst for experience was indefatigable. If he could keep up this pursuit of experience and delight of life in the face of existential and physical pain, surely I could, too.

Taking the train home from his service, I set myself the mission of trying something new every day for a year. I knew enough about the brain to know that it was important to forge new neural networks through repeated action, and make them become more dominant than the pathways that old habits have carved. Alcoholics Anonymous does that for you. But I reckoned other things could, too. Each day I would set myself a task, perform it, and write it up on a blog, which would keep me accountable. I called it *Hey Man, Now You're Really Living* – a title nicked from a song by the Eels about a pessimist who's realised there's a world of wonder out there, if you think to look.

Day one was meditation. Since stopping going to church, aged ten, I'd shied away from anything spiritual or nurturing, so now I tried every kind of new-age treatment I could think of: theta healing in Byron Bay; an electro-psychometer test from a friendly Scientologist; reiki; kinesiology (which made me cry so hard as I lay on my back that my ears filled up); a gong bath; a workshop of singing about angels; eye-movement desensitisation and reprocessing therapy and emotional freedom technique (in which you tap positive confirmations into your meridian lines). I joined a laughter club in a park in Bendigo, attended a neurolinguistics programming seminar packed with hungry entrepreneurs; wore Ben Wa balls to a Metallica concert; got my dreams analysed by *It's Fate* magazine; tried every kind of massage, including one with a happy ending; and had tantric sex with a nice Brazilian practitioner in our matching kimonos.

Hitherto, my risky behaviour had been limited to drug-taking, so I decided to push myself out of my comfort zone with some adrenaline-inducing activities. I tried flying trapeze; flying in a glider; flying in a helicopter; flying a plane; jumping out of a plane; drag-racing in a hot rod; doing donuts in a V8 ute; go-karting; riding a quad bike; riding a jet ski; riding a camel; riding a horse; riding a cow; riding a mechanical bull; shooting Glocks, Magnums, Rugers and rifles; and blowing up a bin with five cans of butane, which rained down on the roof of the house.

Having given up my love of sport around puberty, I got active: paddle-boarding; surfing; fishing; krav maga; pro-wrestling; mixed-martial arts; go-go dancing; breaking into Hanging Rock for a night hike; diving in a kelp forest; being water girl at a footy match; joining a 1980s dance troupe; diving with dolphins; and nude night-swimming. Given I was now living in the country, I enlisted help from locals with my rural skills, such as learning knots, chainsawing, pruning, chopping wood, cracking a whip, and taking my 1997 Ford Falcon to a ute muster.

Apart from my *Hey Man* blog alerting me to potential new interests, I was suddenly spending time with people from all walks of life, all of whom were generous once they got wind of my mission. There was the grizzled guy from Mount Isa who taught me how to lay railway tracks in torrential rain; the kids in the eastern suburbs of Melbourne who let me join in their Chinese Lion Dance training; the loggers in the Otway Ranges who gave me a go on their bulldozer; the cashed-up baby boomers in Apollo Bay who took me on their yacht race; the brass band who let me lead them in a zombie parade at Falls Festival; the farmer who set me to work milking his cows.

From day one, *Hey Man* got to work on my psyche. I had a renewed sense of purpose, a challenge, and a sense of growth, plus it satisfied my sensation-seeking nature. It's true that some people wouldn't have the resources to pull a year-long mission together, either because of a glut of children or a dearth of funds, but if you boil *Hey Man* down to its essence – trying new experiences – it's easy enough to achieve. By using a bit of cheek and nerve, most activities were free anyway. In the case of taking a flight in a glider, I did a U-turn upon passing a field of enthusiasts prepping their planes and asked if one of them would take me up. Two new lessons learned there: if you don't ask, you don't get; and don't assume something is not for the likes of you. In fact, insist that it is.

4. Figure out what you enjoy

I worried that by quitting I would lose my identity, but it's a bit like travelling to far-flung places, in that you find out what you're really made of. If you have come to only enjoy smoking, drinking and their accoutrements, you might have to really excavate to find a new hobby. Here's a hint. Ask yourself what you liked doing as a child. You know, before you latched on to the unholy teat.

Since giving up my residency on bar stools, I volunteer at a kangaroo shelter, an obvious move for someone who was a charity-mugger for the RSPCA as a small child (give me a school fete and I'd hand you in turn a leaflet on factory-farmed pigs). On the way to the shelter, I sing my guts out – great joyous bursts as I traverse the potholed roads of rural Victoria. As an adolescent, my throat clenched up and my voice withered away, so that even when I joined bands I refused to sing backing vocals. I believed singing to be the most expressive thing you could do, and the last thing I wanted to do was reveal myself. Now I'm happy to, because singing is serotonin sucked through a straw (any drinker will tell you that technique gets you drunk quicker). Singing in a vocal group – like a choir or a glee club – is probably the closest you can get to a drunken deep-and-meaningful. Embrace the dork.

The most successful quitters I've met have found one or two solid new habits or hobbies to fill the void. I've got a friend who stopped shooting speed and is now a life coach with her own yoga centre. Another works with Aboriginal communities in Alice Springs, having hallucinogenic experiences of a more spiritual nature. Yet another is a competing body builder who gets the same gory enjoyment out of her four-a.m. starts and rations of food as she did with her four-a.m. crashes and lines of coke. It all taps into the same capacity for endurance. Similarly, many quitters turn to running, gaining increasing highs through races and marathons. They've got a head start with their all-or-nothing mindset.

Sometimes people's new passion will still be based around addiction. I've written this book; others turn to counselling. My friend Wendy used to work on blockbuster reality TV shows and held the contestants in great contempt. Since quitting booze and drugs, she makes documentaries about rehabs, eating disorders, the mentally ill and society's underdogs. 'Now I'm so fucking reasonable and can see both sides of every argument,' she says, 'so perhaps in a way I'm not as good a producer. But it's certainly given me the insight to cover some more complex topics.'

By the way, a 2009 study from University College London found that the average time it takes for a new habit to stick is sixty-six days.

5. Remember you have a body

Stress is a major threat to staying off substances, both in the short term and the long term. Short term, it makes us want to seek out sweet narcotic relief if we don't have a better plan in place. Long term, its neurotoxic effects on the brain undermine the plasticity required for forging new, healthier paths. Unfortunately, for a lot of people, quitting drugs and alcohol coincides with some kind of catastrophe – nobody goes out on a high – so keeping the brain a stress-free zone is no mean feat.

I can't lie. I still haven't managed to meditate more than a handful of times, despite every bit of recovery literature I've ever read advising that it is the absolute best thing you could possibly do; vipassana meditation in particular. People who formerly sought out reverie drugs such as opiates and MDMA, in particular, take to it like a duck to water. Those people would probably score high in 'self-transcendence' in the Temperament and Character Inventory test I took in chapter three, which is the idea of being part of a greater whole, be it through spirituality, humanism, or nature.

For those who prefer stimulants and distraction, like me, the ancient art of meditation is far less appealing than simply soothing the savage beast with a cigarette. My compromise is to pay someone Zen-like to massage my body into self-transcendence on my behalf. That's legit. See also, 'flow state', in which people become so engrossed in what they're doing – gardening, painting, writing – that they pleasantly lose track of time and self.

The bedfellow of meditation is mindfulness. A lot of Buddhist philosophy has trickled into twelve-step programs over the years; everyone's reading Jung and Tolle. Similarly, many drug and alcohol counselling services will offer mindfulness techniques as part of their sessions, such as picturing your physical discomfort and giving it a shape, a colour, or a name, in order to perceive it as just something, not everything. (It's not always recommended for people actively experiencing trauma, though, as the focus on the body can trigger symptoms.) I've come up with my own body-focused exercises to remind myself that I'm not just a mind on a stick; visualising the energy from the ground rising through my feet as I wait for a train, or expanding the sensation of my body out past its boundaries and into the room. It takes every ounce of concentration not to accidentally activate my sacral chakra and loop off into some phallic fantasy, but that's okay.

On that note, sober sex is the greatest. I'm so annoyed at how much good-quality sex with attractive people I could have been having for those two wasted decades, instead of just employing 'the lean' as an evening at the pub progressed, then barely remembering what came next. Now there's the mission, the proposition, and the necessary taking of control, since most sexual partners will be far more freaked out that you're sober than you are of *being* sober.

It's also great to learn the possibilities and limitations of your body through yoga or sport, particularly if you've only subjected your physical self to crushing hangovers and comedowns. I took up pro-wrestling for a spell, learning how to crash satisfyingly loudly onto the canvas, and to bounce off the ropes, onto a bloke swollen with steroids and into a sunset flip. I marvelled at the increasing trust I placed on myself to land correctly or gain enough height.

If you're really not into breaking a sweat, you could always get suspended from hooks in a fetish club.

6. Get drunk on the milk of human kindness

Ex-dopamine jockeys need to expand their horizons: there are other sources of brain bliss to tap.

Serotonin is a neurotransmitter associated with euphoria and contentment. You'll get a boost of it if you take ecstasy or LSD, but also if you contemplate what you're grateful for in your life – a practice recommended by Buddhists and twelve-steppers alike. I additionally make a list at the end of each day of all the positive things I did, from checking in on mates to taking a swim. Forget the negatives if you know you flourish better with encouragement.

Then there's oxytocin, which is known as 'the cuddle chemical' because it's released by nursing mothers, but you'll experience it when bonding, full stop (I'm pretty sure I was flooded with it when I first nuzzled a bottle of whisky). Together, they are the warm and fuzzies, and they are at your disposal.

You'll experience both together when you take part in a group activity. The data from dry-community website *Hello Sunday Morning*, for instance, shows that the more supportive comments a user makes on others' profiles, the higher they rate their own mood.

They're also triggered by empathy and altruism, so volunteer work is a great move. One friend started mentoring teenage boys, the age he was when he took a dive. Another cleans up parks and nature strips, since she used to trash the same with her mates when drunk, and this then led into a job in the environmental sector.

I signed up as a visitor at an aged-care centre. Initially it was penance for deserting my grandfather in his final years. My fondest childhood memories are of our games of backgammon, or of him reading me Roald Dahl, or trying to make me laugh at the dinner table with limericks and bad jokes. As soon as I hit puberty I started withdrawing, and by the time he died in hospital I was entirely caught up in a one-woman soap opera, barely having time to visit him in his final week. I can't ever undo that, but I can pay it forward.

The first resident I visited, Cynthia, was a former artist who bore her unbearably hunched form with a peaceful stoicism. For the past few decades I had been so young and vital, yet so self-absorbed with woe, when it's the elderly who are truly invisible and resigned to mental and physical pain. Cynthia schooled me in fine-art techniques, and I read to her on the night she died.

Another resident, Jim, had served in the forces like my grandfather and even trained at the same base. One day I saw he'd been crying. A relative had turned up at front desk, he said, and had been telling staff stories about him. I had a sinking feeling. They were saying he'd hurt two children, but he would never hurt a child. He was a pacifist, he reminded me.

I'm not a counsellor, so I changed the subject. On the spot, though, I decided to keep seeing Jim. Over the past year we'd formed a genuine bond. Whatever he had or hadn't done, I could recognise there were more facets to him than that. It was helpful to me, too.

I started to notice that residents only chose to recall a small sliver of their lives, usually bridging their twenties and early thirties. That passage of time would either be recalled as their glory days, or the period in which they were mightily hard done by. It made me realise I needed to actively choose which of my narratives I would listen to.

7. Reject your narrative

Ask yourself honestly: Has the narrative you've always told yourself – that you're misunderstood, a victim, deprived, or have an addictive personality – just become a useful excuse? That narrative may well stem from messages you were given in childhood, but have you nurtured and manipulated it to explain away your most dubious decisions?

Having feelings of rejection, shame, guilt, anger and grief – the five emotions I would say drive problematic substance use – are the expected outcomes of adversity. However, at some point there comes the realisation that a choice can be made: whether to get help and build up resilience to the best of your ability, or whether to allow the experience to define you forever and drive your substance use.

In her memoir *Pink Suit for a Blue Day*, Eurogliders singer Grace Knight refers to a catalyst and a legacy. The catalyst in her life, she says, was being sexually abused by her violent father. The legacy was the feeling of worthlessness that she nurtured for forty-five years. That piqued my interest. When I ask Knight about her theory and she explains, 'I realised the physical side of what happened to me as a child was over with the next morning. I gave this thing a life, and from then on I fed and nourished it until it became so monumental that it actually shaped my decisions and character. It became the filter I would grow through.'

While it would have been the messages that Knight received from her family following those events that really kickstarted that 'nourishment', her concept of catalyst and legacy is useful to me. The catalyst would be different for everyone. It could be a car accident that left the survivor needing pain relief that got out of hand. It could be a messy divorce that led to a bottle of wine a night. It could be grief; survivor guilt; the children leaving home. The legacy is dictated by the messages you received that you have invested in, and by the limitations of your resilience.

The difficulty is, letting go of the legacy and bringing more positive narratives to the fore means facing up to the fact that any bad decisions made from that point forth are yours and yours alone. For me, making that decision to take full responsibility for my actions from now on (no, I'm not going to backdate it to my youthful decisions) felt like taking off my armbands and jumping into the deep end: scary, but liberating.

8. Set your own sobriety agenda

Traditionally, any book with an addiction-memoir element should involve the author turning over every rock to examine the nasty things that squirm beneath. Then there's a hasty crescendo, in the final chapter, to redemption. The narrator is suddenly a goodly sober, saved by their eternal pledge to recovery. The reader, only a second ago skidding in gory detail, is now showered with rose petals. Or, rather, pelted with sobriety chips.

I'm a flawed narrator, then. I don't call myself 'sober'. That's partly because the term reminds me of 'sombre', 'sob,' and 'so boring', but partly because, since stopping drinking, I've taken drugs. I ate a hash cookie at a dinner party. I accept a Valium from time to time. A psychedelic in the spirit of self-exploration. And then there's been silly, teenage stuff for the ridiculousness of it – a whiff of poppers while strolling through Pigalle, a balloon of nitrous in front of the TV. This freedom was a decision I made about two years into total abstinence, and it's about joyous bursts, rather than grinding self-medication.

Personally, having that pressure-relief valve feels safer to me. Telling myself 'you can if you want' doesn't provoke the imp in my brain into leaping for the chandeliers because, as we all know, being given permission to do something immediately takes away the appeal. By contrast, telling myself I'm abstinent for life might result in an almighty blowout one day as the pressure builds. No system is infallible.

There will be people reading this with anger burning in their heart. To someone who is truly sober, my generous 'you can if you want' self-policy borders on betrayal. I know how that feels. I remember when a couple who had quit drinking told me that they'd each had a beer at a wedding, and reported with pleasure that they didn't enjoy the beer and now they knew they didn't need to wonder about it again. I felt an inexplicable fury. For me, alcohol was an absolute no-go zone; never worth risking. So that was really the root of my rage – that they'd made a decision that had worked out just fine for them, but it threatened my new blueprint for life.

Whatever your personal policy, drug and alcohol treatment shouldn't be one-size-fits-all – and it isn't, if you properly investigate what's on offer. According to the 2001–02 survey of 43,000 Americans by the National Institute of Alcohol Abuse and Alcoholism, more than half of those individuals who overcame alcohol dependence did so by cutting back rather than completely abstaining.

While some people classify as hardcore poly-drug users, most people have a leaning towards one type, such as sedatives, or stimulants. I mentioned Professor Marc Lewis earlier. He doesn't shoot up anymore, but he enjoys a glass of wine. 'I don't imagine I could continue moderate use of opiates,' he tells me, 'but a drink is okay for me because it's not my drug of choice.'

Bill Wilson, the co-founder of Alcoholics Anonymous, quit drinking in the thirties but experimented with LSD with

Aldous Huxley in the 1950s. He even hoped LSD could prove to be beneficial to those in recovery. These days, debates rage on recovery forums as to whether opioid replacement therapy (such as methadone) is okay for NA members, or whether a 'marijuana maintenance plan' is acceptable when attending AA, but certainly it would be completely viable to go to an outpatient drug and alcohol service and ask for a plan that includes, say, controlled pot use in order to support the quitting of something else.

Geoff Corbett is a senior clinician who works with young adults in Brisbane. He tells me, 'There are always going to be outliers that AA and NA can put on a pedestal, but there will be another thousand people that AA and NA won't work for, which is why we provide options. If we work from a harm-minimisation framework, abstinence can be at one end and safer use can be at the other end. The client chooses options in between. It requires good assessment and really good treatment planning to look at achievable goals and put some parameters into place. We keep in mind that a person's life is in flux and we can move the goalposts any time we want.'

Hello Sunday Morning also has a flexible approach to tackling alcohol use. 'Nowhere do we dictate what a person has to do to be a part of *Hello Sunday Morning*,' says founder Chris Raine. 'Our wording – "reassessing your relationship with alcohol" – turns it into a subjective experience. Even government campaigns are starting to use that kind of wording, and that's a good cultural shift. It's not about "Are you an alcoholic?" "Are you addicted or not?" It's about "What relationship with alcohol would you like?" It could be none; it could be some.'

Certainly for some people, abstinence really is the only safe option – and they know that. There's a spectrum of severity, and I can't compare my former levels of dependence to, say, the brother of one of my closest friends who died after continuing drinking post–liver transplant, or my mate who winds up in hospital or a psych ward every time she drinks. If you're thinking of quitting something, why not at least try both a twelve-step meeting and a treatment service and find what works better for you?

The most important thing is to accept that mistakes, lapses, relapses, busts, lessons, errant evenings, experimental breaks – whatever you want to call them – are statistically likely no matter what route you choose. It means maintaining vigilance for old behaviours creeping back in, whether it's six months, five years, or twenty years after you've curtailed your habits. Vigilance, purposefulness, meaningfulness, curiosity, goals and altruism – they're your new stash. Keep them close.

ACKNOWLEDGEMENTS

I was blown away by the generosity of many people during the writing of *Woman of Substances*. The biggest thank you goes to my family for trusting me, and for no doubt moving many mental roadblocks to accommodate my need to write this book. Once I shelved my initial idea of quietly putting it out and hoping they wouldn't notice, they made themselves available by reading chapters and recommending articles, and Mum took on much transcribing, or 'mumscribing' – a job that really does demand unconditional love.

In order to explore the nature of my own substance dependence, I tumbled into a vortex of pathological scrutiny. I realised afterwards, once I'd signed off on the book, that I skimped on the love, support and good times. Certainly they're more obvious now (who really basks in those good fortunes in their twenties anyway?), but they were always there from family and friends, keeping me afloat. To this end, *Woman of Substances* is a memoir of addiction, not a memoir of a girl.

Thank you also to my husband, Justin, who keeps his reserves of pragmatic advice and unswerving support well topped up. I met Justin when he was running one of the many bars I'd zigzag into on my way home, just before I quit. He'd thud my glass of wine down in front of me impassively, pause, and turn away. I took it to be judgement, since I would have had a Joker smile of red wine by this point, but when I bumped into him years later I realised he just had a lovely deadpan face. He has built us a happy home in more ways than one.

And thank you to Esther Coleman-Hawkins, for going above, beyond and all the way through. Thank god you're here.

Cheers to those friends who read bits and offered support: 'Tim' and 'Alex' (your responses meant the world to me); 'Sylvia and Gino'; Wayan Arnup; Anita Ashpole; Lucy Carolan; Jack Colwell; Lee Kofman; Nicola Redhouse and Wyndham Wallace. Hearty cheers to the cheer squad: Kate Hyde; Brigid Delaney; Kelly Doust; Kate Holden; Sheridan Wright; Rhonda, Tim and the gang at Cohoots in Castlemaine; and the Munn, Dimovski and Valentish tribes for staying fast. Dr Matthew Gullo and Dr Natalie Loxton for allowing me quite the back and forth; Dr Monica Barratt, Dr Adrian Carter and Lisa Kunde for being my unofficial sounding boards; Dr Naomi Crafti, my graduate-certificate supervisor at Turning Point, who oversaw the early drafts of 'Total Control'; Geoff Corbett – clinician and SixFtHick frontman – for so many conversations about AOD treatment; Ben Corbett and Loki Lockwood for permission to use the lyrics in chapter six. Everyone at Black Inc, especially Team *WoS*: editor and publisher Aviva Tuffield for leaping upon the idea; Kate Nash; Erin Sandiford and Sophy Williams. You all made this process a dream.

Thank you also to interviewees, unofficial fact-checkers and go-betweens: Paul Aiken and Donna Ribton-Turner at ReGen; Professor Steve Allsop; Professor Amanda Baker; Dr Joanne Bryant; Ilka Burnham-King, Kit Kavanagh-Ryan and everybody else at the Alcohol & Drug Foundation; Dr Adrian Carter; Katrina Chamberlain; Professor Jan Copeland; Paul Dillon; Dr Genevieve Dingle; Sunny Drake; Dr Nadine Ezard; Dr Matthew Gullo; Dr Janet Hammill; Professor Wayne Hall; Associate Professor Rob Hester; Gabriella Holmes; Dr Jennifer Johnston; the Kamira Farm Team; Professor Jayashri Kulkarni; Associate Professor Nicole Lee; Professor Marc Lewis; Andrew McMillen; Glenda Milne at Guthrie House; Christine Ockenfels and the Holyoake team; Gina Pera; Paul Quigley; Chris Raine at *Hello Sunday Morning*; Jane Rowe at the Mirabel Foundation; Dr James Rowe; Professor Tim Slade; Matt Tilley; Professor Jane Ussher; Melissa Warner and Martin Whitely. Particular thanks to Anni Hine Moana, whom I met during the existential-crisis stage of this book, and whose encouragement came at a pivotal moment.

You can read related stories at: www.womanofsubstances.com

SELECTED READING

The following literature was specifically referred to in the preceding chapters. A full bibliography of studies that informed the book can be found at: www.womanofsubstances.com

Chapter 1: The Petri Dish of You

ABC (2017), *Life at Seven: Tackling Temperament*, retrieved from www.abc.net.au/tv/life/the_science/TACKLINGTEMPERAMENT.htm

Australian Institute of Family Studies (2016), *Australian Temperament Project*, retrieved from www3.aifs.gov.au/atp

Centers for Disease Control and Prevention (2016), *Adverse Childhood Experiences (ACEs)*, retrieved from https://www.cdc.gov/violenceprevention/acestudy/index.html

Meaney, M.J., Brake, W. & Gratton, A. (2002), 'Environmental regulation of the development of mesolimbic dopamine systems: a neurobiological mechanism for vulnerability to drug abuse?', *Psychoneuroendocrinology*, 27(1), 127–138.

Chapter 2: Baby Misogynist

AIHW (2014), *National Drug Strategy Household Survey detailed report*: 2013. Drug statistics series no. 28. Cat. no. PHE 183. Canberra: AIHW.

Hyde, Z., Doherty, M., Tilley, P.M., McCaul, K., Rooney, R. & Jancey, J. (2014), *The First Australian National Trans Mental Health Study: Summary of results*, Curtin University, School of Public Health.

Khantzian, E.J. (2012), 'Reflections on treating addictive disorders: a psychodynamic perspective', *The American Journal on Addictions*, 21(3), 274–279.

Shipton, D., Whyte, B. & Walsh, D. (2013), 'Alcohol-related mortality in deprived UK cities: worrying trends in young women challenge recent national downward trends', *Journal of Epidemiology and Community Health*.

Chapter 3: Chaos Theory

Kong, G., Smith, A.E., McMahon, T.J., Cavallo, D.A., Schepis, T.S., Desai, R.A. & Krishnan-Sarin, S. (2013), 'Pubertal status, sensation-seeking, impulsivity, and substance use in high-school-aged boys and girls', *Journal of Addiction Medicine*, 7(2), 116.

White, A.M., Truesdale, M.C., Bae, J.G., Ahmad, S., Wilson, W.A., Best, P.J. & Swartzwelder, H.S. (2002), 'Differential effects of ethanol on motor coordination in adolescent and adult rats', *Pharmacology, Biochemistry and Behavior*, 73(3), 673–677.

Chapter 4: Total Control

Englander, E. (2012), *Digital Self-Harm: Frequency, Type, Motivations and Outcomes*, retrieved from: http://webhost.bridgew.edu/marc/DIGITAL%20SELF%20HARM%20report.pdf

Kane, T.A., Loxton, N., Staiger, P. & Dawe, S. (2004), 'Does the tendency to act impulsively underlie binge eating and binge drinking problems? An empirical investigation', *Personality and Individual Differences*, 36, 83–94.

Loxton, N.J. & Dawe, S. (2001), 'Alcohol abuse and dysfunctional eating in adolescent girls: the influence of individual differences in sensitivity to reward and punishment', *International Journal of Eating Disorders*, 29(4), 455–462.

National Center on Addiction and Substance Abuse (CASA) (2003), *Food for Thought: Substance Abuse and Eating Disorders*, retrieved from: http://www.centeronaddiction.org/addiction-research/reports/food-thought-substance-abuse-and-eating-disorders

Ressler, A. (2008), 'Insatiable hungers: eating disorders and substance abuse', *Social Work Today*, 8(4), 30.

Vandereycken, W. & Van Humbeeck, I. (2008), 'Denial and concealment of eating disorders: a retrospective survey', *European Eating Disorders Review*, 16(2), 109–114.

Chapter 5: Amateur Alchemy

Back, S.E., Payne, R., Waldrop, A.E., Smith, A., Reeves, S. & Brady, K.T. (2009), 'Prescription opioid aberrant behaviors: a pilot study of gender differences, *The Clinical Journal of Pain*, 25(6), 477.

Mancebo, Maria C. et al (2009), 'Substance use disorders in an obsessive compulsive disorder clinical sample', *Journal of Anxiety Disorders*, 23(4), 429–435

Ruscio, A. M., Stein, D. J., Chiu, W.T. & Kessler, R. C. (2010), 'The epidemiology of obsessive-compulsive disorder in the National Comorbidity Survey Replication', *Molecular Psychiatry*, 15, 53–63.

van Emmerik-van Oortmerssen, K., van de Glind, G., van den Brink, W., Smit, F., Crunelle, C.L., Swets, M. & Schoevers, R.A. (2012), 'Prevalence of attention-deficit hyperactivity disorder in substance use disorder patients: a meta-analysis and meta-regression analysis', *Drug and Alcohol Dependence*, 122(1), 11–19.

Whitely, M. (2011), *Perth's Dexamphetamine Hangover*, retrieved from: http://speedupsitstill.com/2011/07/19/perth%E2%80%99s-dexamphetamine-hangover-3/

Chapter 6: A Crude Form of Seduction

Bryant, J. & Treloar, C. (2007), 'The gendered context of initiation to injecting drug use: evidence for women as active initiates', *Drug and Alcohol Review*, 26(3), 287–293.

Rowe, J. (2011), *Shantusi: surveying HIV and need in the unregulated sex industry*, Inner South Community Health Service: Melbourne.

Stevens, R. (2015), 'Mother of three reveals devastating impact of ice', *Northern Star*, retrieved from: http://www.northernstar.com.au/news/casino-ice-addict-warns-destroys-life/2646522/

Chapter 7: Pretty Intense

Angell, M. (2011), 'The illusions of psychiatry', *The New York Review of Books*, retrieved from http://www.nybooks.com/articles/2011/07/14/illusions-of-psychiatry/

Blue Knot Foundation (n.d.), *Complex Trauma and Trauma-Informed Practice Guidelines*, retrieved from: http://www.blueknot.org.au/ABOUT-US/Our-Documents/Practice-Guidelines

Holland, Julie (ed.) (2001), *Ecstasy: The Complete Guide: a comprehensive look at the risks and benefits of MDMA.*

Kaplan, M. (1983), 'A woman's view of *DSM-III*', *American Psychologist*, 38(7), 786–792.

Sansone, R.A. & Sansone, L.A. (2011), 'Substance use disorders and borderline personality: common bedfellows', *Innovations in Clinical Neuroscience*, 8(9), 10–13

Chapter 8: Collateral Damage

Holly, J. (2013), 'Not worth reporting: women's experiences of drug-facilitated sexual assault', AVA, retrieved from https://avaproject.org.uk/

wp/wp-content/uploads/2016/03/Not-worth-reporting-Full-report.pdf
Taylor, N., Prichard, J. & Charlton, K. (2004), *National Project on Drink Spiking: Investigating the Nature and Extent of Drink Spiking in Australia*, retrieved from http://aic.gov.au/media_library/archive/publications-2000s/national-project-on-drink-spiking-investigating-the-nature-and-extent-of-drink-spiking-in-australia.pdf

Chapter 9: Body of Evidence

Allen, N., Beral, V., Casabonne, D., Kan, S., Reeves, G., Brown, A. & Green, J. (2009), 'Moderate alcohol intake and cancer incidence in women', *Journal of the National Cancer Institute*, 101(5), 296–305.
Burd, L., Blair, J. & Dropps, K. (2012), 'Prenatal alcohol exposure, blood alcohol concentrations and alcohol elimination rates for the mother, fetus and newborn', *Journal of Perinatology*, 32(9), 652–659.
Lee, H.J. et al (2013), 'Transgenerational effects of paternal alcohol exposure in mouse offspring', *Animal Cells and Systems*, 17(6), 429–434.
van Dijken, G., Blom, R., Hene, R. & Boer, W. (2013), 'High incidence of mild hyponatraemia in females using ecstasy at a rave party', *Nephrology Dialysis Transplantation*, 28(9), 2277–2283.

Chapter 10: Your Brain as a Pokie Machine

Linnet, J., Peterson, E., Doudet, D., Gjedde, A. & Møller, A. (2010), 'Dopamine release in ventral striatum of pathological gamblers losing money', *Acta Psychiatrica Scandinavica*, 122(4), 326–333.
Lewis, M. (2015), 'Two yous – a disconnect in mind and brain', retrieved from http://www.memoirsofanaddictedbrain.com/connect/two-yous-a-disconnect-in-mind-and-brain/
Takahashi, H., Kato, M., Matsuura, M., Mobbs, D., Suhara, T. & Okubo, Y. (2009), 'When your gain is my pain and your pain is my gain: neural correlates of envy and schadenfreude', *Science*, 323(5916), 937–939.

Chapter 11: The Geographical

Holmes, A., Fitzgerald, P., MacPherson, K., DeBrouse, L., Colacicco, G. & Flynn, S. et al. (2012), 'Chronic alcohol remodels prefrontal neurons and disrupts NMDAR-mediated fear extinction encoding', *Nature Neuroscience*, 15(10), 1359–1361.

Chapter 12: 52 Observations

Seo, D., Lacadie, C.M., Tuit, K., Hong, K., Constable, R.T. & Sinha, R. (2013), 'Disrupted ventromedial prefrontal function, alcohol craving, and subsequent relapse risk', *JAMA Psychiatry*, 70(7), 727–739.

Chapter 13: A Word from My Sponsor

Large, W. & Johnson, F. (1980), 'Psychiatric diagnosis on acute admission related to prevailing weather conditions', *Psychopathology*, 13(2), 90–95.

Chapter 14: Keeping Mum

Kilroy, D. (2016), *Women in Prison in Australia*, retrieved from https://njca.com.au/wp-content/uploads/2015/04/Kilroy-Debbie-Women-in-Prison-in-Australia-paper.pdf

Lucke, J. & Hall, W. (2012), 'Under what conditions is it ethical to offer incentives to encourage drug-using women to use long-acting forms of contraception?', *Addiction*, 107(6), 1036–1041.

Spinney, A. (2016), 'FactCheck Q&A: are Indigenous women 34–80 times more likely than average to experience violence?' *The Conversation*, retrieved from http://theconversation.com/factcheck-qanda-are-indigenous-women-34-80-times-more-likely-than-average-to-experience-violence-61809

Chapter 15: A Call to Arms

Covington, S. (2008), 'Women and addiction: a trauma-informed approach', *Journal of Psychoactive Drugs*, 40(supplement 5), 377–385.

Duggan, M. (2016), *Investing in Women's Mental Health: Strengthening the Foundations for Women, Families and the Australian Economy*. Policy Issues paper No. 2016-02.

Hill, R. (2016), 'Sex differences in animal models of schizophrenia shed light on the underlying pathophysiology,' *Neuroscience & Biobehavioral Reviews*, 67, 41–56.

Network of Alcohol and Other Drugs Agencies (2016), *What's Gender Got to Do with It?* Retrieved from http://nada.org.au/nada-focus-areas/women/whats-gender-got-to-do-with-it-forum/

Slade, T., Chapman, C., Tesson, M. (2016), 'Women's alcohol consumption catching up to men: why this matters', retrieved from https://newsroom.unsw.edu.au/news/health/women's-alcohol-consumption-catching-men-why-matters

Chapter 16: Choose Your Own Adventure

NIAAA Spectrum (2009), 'Alcoholism isn't what it used to be', retrieved from https://www.spectrum.niaaa.nih.gov/archives/v1i1Sept2009/features/Alcoholism.html

University College London (2009), 'How long does it take to form a habit?', retrieved from http://www.ucl.ac.uk/news/news-articles/0908/09080401

RESOURCES

Alcoholics Anonymous
aa.org.au/findameeting

Family Drug Support
1300 368 186
fds.org.au

Hello Sunday Morning
hellosundaymorning.org

Narcotics Anonymous
na.org.au

SMART Recovery
smartrecoveryaustralia.com.au

Soberistas
soberistas.com

TouchBase (LGBTI services)
touchbase.org.au

Women for Sobriety
womenforsobriety.org

And various helplines across Australia
livesofsubstance.org/resources-information